We Fight On...
We Fight To Win

A Twin's Battle Against Lymphatic Cancer

First Published in 1996
by
The Limited Edition Press,
633 Liverpool Road, Southport. PR8 3NG
Reprinted October 1996.

Type-set in Century Schoolbook 10/12

We Fight On...
We Fight To Win
A Twin's Battle Against Lymphatic Cancer

Michael A. Ridge
with Steven K. Titherington

❖❖❖❖❖❖❖

Limited Edition Press

A LIMITED EDITION BOOK

CONTENTS

*Items in the text are indicated by an asterisk

Andrew

June 1992

Dedication

To Andrew,
This book is dedicated to your heroism.
With undying love
Mum, Dad, Natalie and Michael.

Did you ever know that you're my hero,
You're everything I would like to be,
And I can fly higher than an eagle,
For you are the wind beneath my wings.
(From the film 'Beaches' copyright 1990)

August 1996

ANDREW AND MICHAEL

ANDREW NEIL AND MICHAEL ANTHONY RIDGE were born at 12:25pm and 12:40pm respectively on 27th July 1970 at Christiana Hartley Maternity Hospital, Southport. Their early education between 1975-81 took place at Woodvale County Primary School. In 1981 they moved to Ainsdale High School where they successfully achieved 9 'O' levels each. Between 1986 and 1988 they went to King George V Sixth Form College, Southport, where Andrew studied A levels in Maths, Chemistry and Economics and Michael studied Chemistry, Geography and Geology. After successfully completing their A levels it was time to go their separate ways, or so they thought! In October 1988 Andrew went to Keble College, Oxford to read Chemistry and Michael went to Collingwood College, Durham to read Geography. Unfortunately Oxford did not turn out to be the best move for Andrew and in February 1989 he decided to leave, working at Royal Life Insurance in Liverpool as a Clerical Assistant for 4 months. In October 1989 Andrew started his chemistry degree again as a first year undergraduate at Collingwood College, Durham.

Michael graduated with a 2:1 honours in Geography in June 1991 and decided to train to be a geography teacher. In June 1992 Andrew graduated with 1st Class Honours in Chemistry and decided to remain at Durham to do a 3 year PhD in Organic Chemistry. He was in his final year of postgraduate research when he was taken ill. Since Andrew's death at 6.50am on Wednesday 18th October 1995, Michael continues to teach geography at Brownedge St Mary's R.C. High School, Bamber Bridge, near Preston where he has been since September 1993. He is an active member of his local church where he is just about to start his third and final years training for Lay Reader ministry in the Church of England.

Acknowledgements

I am particularly grateful to my parents, for all their love and support and for helping me to clarify some of the events in this book. Thanks also go to the Rev. Ken Owen and Michelle for proof reading and commenting on the accuracy of the text.

I am indebted to Andrew's consultant Dr Patrick Chu, at the Royal Liverpool Hospital for helping me with the medical aspects of the story and providing detailed answers to several questions relating to Andrew's illness. I am also grateful to Ward 7Y and associated Doctors and Consultants for allowing me to use their names and to Ann Brown, Haematology Counsellor for her help and support.

My biggest thanks must go to my friend Steven Titherington. He has done most of the donkey work in typing up the text and his word processing and computing skills have been invaluable. Without his Christian love and commitment this book would never have come to fruition. Not forgetting also Mrs Titherington who provided endless cups of tea!

Thank You.

Michael A. Ridge

August 1996

INTRODUCTION

THIS BOOK tells the story of a 25 year old student's fight against Non-Hodgkins Lymphoma (a malignant disease of the Lymph nodes) and how faith and courage triumphed over hopelessness and despair. For forty-one weeks during 1995 Andrew Ridge received treatment at a specialist cancer centre. It charts the simplified medical history of Andrew's disease in a way which the non-specialist will find readable but deals with far more than the progression of Andrew's disease. It is focused on the inspirational bravery of a young man who refused to give up hope and how God used a situation of great suffering to cause a local church to fall on its knees in prayer. It provides insight into the depth of human relationships which exist between patient, nursing staff, doctors and relatives and is valuable reading for any Christian who is faced with a similar challenge of fighting or caring for a member of the family who has cancer.

CHAPTER ONE

COLD AT CHRISTMAS

WHEN ANDREW returned from Durham on Thursday 8th December 1994 to spend the weekend "getting rid of a bad cold" we had never in our wildest dreams imagined that this was the beginning of a serious illness which would affect us for nearly the whole of 1995.

Andrew was a typical postgraduate student who was studying at the Department of Chemistry, University of Durham and researching into Asymmetric Organic Synthesis as part of a three year Ph.D. He had studied for three years between 1989-1992 to gain a 1st class honours degree in Chemistry and it was a natural progression to carry on studying for an extra 3 years, especially if it meant delaying getting a proper job! A typical student, he arrived home with a bin-bag full of dirty washing in his A reg "rust bucket" of a Metro, which was as usual full of junk. Christmas was approaching and the family were looking forward to a quiet Christmas together. Andrew's first visit to his local GP led him to being given some antibiotics and being told to come back in a couple of weeks. The cold didn't go away, it just appeared to get worse and Andrew wasn't really interested in eating much. I was beginning to feel a bit frustrated. Here was Christmas approaching and after a busy term at school I was looking forward to spending some time with my brother and doing some socialising, but he was stuck in bed with this cold. "Oh come on Andrew," I felt like saying, "It's only a cold for goodness sake. Get yourself sorted and then we can have a good Christmas." If only I had known. I would never have thought such an insensitive thought. A second visit to the GP led to some new antibiotics being given so perhaps he would start to feel better in a couple of days. He had also been prescribed some Ammonium Chloride cough mixture to try to help his cough.

Christmas came and everyone wanted to know where Andy was. "Oh, he's got a bad cold, he's a bit under the weather so he's not coming to Midnight Mass." Christmas day we had our usual present opening and Christmas lunch. Andrew even managed some turkey and stuffing and then we had a drive out to Lytham St Annes in the afternoon, although this was curtailed because Andrew was coughing in the car and didn't feel comfortable.

Between Christmas and New Year Andrew was having difficulty in sleeping and getting comfortable, he still had a bad cold and he was also looking rather yellow in colour, rather jaundiced. At last, on his third visit to the GP the doctor decided to send him to Southport Infirmary for a chest x-ray. I remember taking him and dropping him near the front entrance because he was cold and tired. I sat with him with his white cloak on as we waited to be called. The radiographer called him and he had his X-ray and was told to wait. Then I vividly recall the lady coming out and saying "Mr Ridge, could you come back again. We just want to do one more X-ray?" or words to that effect. I thought, that seems a bit strange asking him to come back. I thought nothing of it. The next day, Andrew's GP was on the phone. The X-ray was already with the GP and yet they had told us at the infirmary that usually it takes one week for the results to reach the doctor. There was some fluid on Andrew's lungs which was probably the reason why he was having difficulty lying on one side. The doctor had arranged an urgent appointment with the consultant at Southport District General on Tuesday 3rd January 1995. My Mum didn't seem too pleased with the doctor on the phone because this didn't seem like an urgent appointment, but in retrospect with the New Year fast approaching it was probably the first available appointment. My mother had also asked if the doctor had noticed that Andrew was jaundiced when he had come to the surgery but unfortunately he hadn't. I went to collect the letter from the GP which was informing Andrew of his appointment with a chest consultant. The doctor had said, "Try not to worry. It could be several things. It could be pneumonia, or a chest infection or it could be Lymphoma, a mild form of cancer. We will have to wait and see what the consultant says." Suddenly what had appeared to be a cold had snowballed into something a lot more serious and it was clear that Andrew was very poorly, more than we could have imagined.

I went up to Durham on New Years Eve to collect some of Andrew's valuables. I had visited the wonderful Norman Cathedral at Durham in the afternoon and lit a candle and said a prayer for Andrew. After spending my New Year with a friend I came back to Southport on New Years Day and set up Andrew's CD player so he could listen to some music whilst lying in bed. The cough was still causing him discomfort and it was beginning to cause tension in the house as we desperately waited for 2 pm on Tuesday 3rd January.

New Year came and went. We set off to the hospital. Andy, my friend Cuan who had volunteered to drive, and myself arrived at the hospital at 2pm. There then followed a long wait. This was the beginning of what was going to be ages and ages of waiting in hospital rooms and corridors. It's amazing what you can read in a hospital waiting room, they even have your horoscopes displayed on the television screen so you can see what the future holds before seeing your consultant to see what the future holds!

Dr Serlin and his assistant, a young Asian lady, were both very caring and concerned about Andrew. They asked a series of questions, gave Andrew an examination and then said they wanted to send Andy for a *C.T. Scan and some blood tests in order to try and investigate the reason for his being so poorly. "Would you be able to stay in hospital tonight Andrew?" My parents were desperate to get Andrew hospitalised because of our growing concern. Andrew was admitted to Southport District General on Tuesday 3rd January . We all went to bed and slept soundly. Little did we know what an almighty shock the next day was going to bring.

CHAPTER TWO

SHOCK WAVES

ELEVEN YEARS AGO, in July 1984 my twin brother and I had stepped onto the "hallowed turf" of Anfield Football Ground. Not I might add to watch or partake in a football match! This would have been an anathema to two Evertonians! No, we were making a commitment to Christ after listening to the powerful message of the gospel which had been preached by Billy Graham, an American evangelist in his Mission England crusade. Not only did we become Christians together, we went to school together and eventually, after Andrew had dropped out of Oxford University and worked at Royal Life Insurance we ended up at Durham together, although Andrew was a year behind and I was studying a more 'vocational' subject like Geography instead of Chemistry! We had always done everything together and we had always been the best of friends. Little did I know that this special closeness and relationship we had was about to be put to the ultimate test.

It was a cold and dull Wednesday morning, the 4th January 1995. A typical day for having to get up early and go back to work. I was at school in the morning. I read the reading in the prayers before the staff meeting and then we were back into the normal timetable and after lunch I was teaching. It must have been around 1:45pm when the reprographics lady came into my room and told me there was a phone call. I didn't really think anything as I went to the print room to pick up the phone. It was Mum and she sounded rather quiet and anxious. "Is there anything wrong?" "Yes Michael, do you think you could come home? The doctor rang this morning and they are moving Andrew to the Royal Liverpool Hospital; they think he has got

Leukaemia." I went numb. Time seemed to stand still. I couldn't believe it and will never forget that dreadful moment when the reality hit me. Andrew has got cancer. I don't believe it! It can't be true! The next 30 minutes are all a haze. I remember going down to tell the Deputy Head I would have to go home. In fact my parents where coming to pick me up and we were going straight to Liverpool to see the doctors. I stood in the foyer at school looking out of the window at a grey and miserable Wednesday afternoon, sobbing and wondering if this was all a nightmare and whether I would suddenly wake up and all around would be fine. It is the biggest lesson I have learned - that we have to face the reality in life otherwise we become prisoners of our fear. I had God to trust in and depend on. I was silently praying: "Lord, keep Andy safe. Be with him." Eventually my parents arrived after what seemed like a tremendous wait. I sat in the back as we drove back towards Liverpool and they told me the story. How all the blood samples had been abnormal, how the ward sister had said how sorry she was. How the consultant haematologist at Southport had come to see Andrew and spoken to Mum telling her that Andrew had a very serious blood disorder and they were trying to get him a bed at the Haematology Unit in the Royal Liverpool Hospital which is a specialist centre. I still felt fearful and numb with shock.

We arrived at the Royal and it was a dark and blustery night by now. I looked up at this enormous building. A concrete monstrosity looming up into the night sky. About eleven floors of it. It was a huge place. At least to someone who had little experience of hospital it was. Andrew had already been admitted by ambulance after transferring him from Southport. We had to go to the Haematology Unit which my father figured out was Ward 7Y, a strange coincidence because my Form Group at school was 7Y as well! We got up to the ward and were met by one of the staff nurses who was a pretty girl with a well made up face who showed us to the day-room whilst we waited to see the doctor. We were met by a Dr Wright who was a Senior Registrar and a doctor specialising in Haematology. He told us that they suspected Andrew had a form of cancer called *Non-Hodgkins

Lymphoma which they would have to try and confirm by doing a series of tests. They were planning on taking a sample of bone marrow and they had taken some more blood tests and Andrew was going to start some antibiotics because he was seriously ill. By now I was dying to see Andrew and couldn't even begin to imagine how he was feeling. We walked down the corridor and I remember the many portraits on the wall and we were shown into the last ward, Room 6. Andrew was in the second bed on the right. He was attached to a drip and we went over and had a chat. He seemed to be OK and in good spirits although I do not really remember everything very clearly.

We talked and then we decided to have a chat to the staff nurse because we needed to clarify some of the things that were going to be happening. One of the things I remember from that first conversation was the nurse telling us that there will be lots of people who talk about the disease Andrew has, because their relatives and family have had it, and there is a good chance or a poor chance, or they had this or that treatment, or there was this prognosis or that. It was best to remember that every individual's disease is unique to them and therefore it is unwise to take other peoples experiences as identical or examples to follow. One thing was clear, and I had not really realised this until after Andrew's death, was that we were dealing with a very serious disease. We never asked for a prognosis, because at the end of the day we had already decided that we were going to fight whatever the likely outcome. All I can say is that I believe the prognosis was poor even at the beginning.

After saying our goodbyes to Andy and promising to see him tomorrow and say our prayers for him, we decided it was time to make tracks as all three of us were exhausted and Andrew had only been in hospital one day! We drove back to Ainsdale and as we arrived home my mother's two sisters were waiting after driving over from Burnley. There was much hugging and tears and after we had churned out all the information (which was to be the first of many information bulletins to hundreds of people!) my aunties said goodbye. We stood in the hall - Mum, Dad, Auntie Linda, Myself and Auntie Joyce - in a large embrace. I remember my Mum's oldest sister saying, "Be strong and support each other." It was certainly the time to be a close family and to try to help each other because this was the start of an exhausting year. I went to bed shattered but I felt that God was with me and Andy as well. He would show us his face and his glory and all that was required was faith and trust. "If you love me, do as I command," says Jesus.

CHAPTER THREE

CHEMOTHERAPY BEGINS

ANDREW spent that first weekend in hospital and my sister Natalie came down from Scotland to be able to see Andrew and so we could all be together as a family. It has been very difficult for Natalie. Living in St Andrews, Fife and being so far away from home it is very difficult not to become isolated and not feel part of what was going on. In the end Natalie decided to come down every month (unless she had to rush down for an emergency, which happened on two occasions) and we all tried our best to keep her as fully informed as possible on every aspect of Andrew's treatment. This was something we became experts at. The phone never stopped ringing in the Ridge household in 1995 and my sister would ring every night as I returned from hospital (on the evening shift!) between 9:30 - 10:00pm. I have spent endless amounts of change on the hospital phone outside 7Y ringing friends to ask them to pray and ringing Natalie to pass on any particular news, whether encouraging, discouraging or non-eventful! This is fundamentally important as I look back on Andrew's illness and gain a new perspective, keeping people informed as much as possible in order to make prayer specific and targeted and also, more importantly, making people feel that they are included and have a part to play in Andrew's struggle. This story is not supposed to be about giving advice, but having the information at our fingertips and being able to pass it on to people at church to keep them updated, was invaluable and helped Andrew tremendously in the long months that lay ahead.

Andrew met his consultant on the Thursday. A lovely Chinese gentleman called Dr Chu who explained that Andrew was going to go to Broadgreen Cardiothorasic Centre on Monday for a biopsy on Tuesday in order to get a sample of Lymph node and get a precise diagnosis. He also told Andrew and Mum that he would be having some form of Chemotherapy which would have to be decided on and that it was going to be a "very long haul" which basically meant we were in for a tremendously draining year. These were the first of many ward rounds where the Haematology team, usually consisting of the Consultant, Senior Registrar, a handful of Senior House & House Officers and a Counsellor would come and update Andrew and our parents on the progress and what was happening in regard to his treatment. Although it was a sad year in many ways, the ward rounds provided occasional times of lightheartedness and banter as well as the usually sad and pessimistic looks depending on who the consultant was that particular month. My parents were there for most of these times because I was usually at work, but I did manage to sit in on several of them. I used to feel my stomach churn and the butterflies going round as they walked slowly round the room and then came to Andrew's bed! I spent a year of looking at anxious faces and listening intently to every word that was said. Somehow these people used to strike me as so powerful, as though everything they did and said, Andrew's life depended on it. I had to keep reminding myself that Andrew was ultimately in God's hands and the medical prowess was a gift from God. All I can say is that there is a tremendous awe attached to a consultant in a brilliant white coat walking down the corridor with an entourage of doctors, nurses and counsellor following on behind. We need to be grateful to God for men and women such as the ones I met at the Royal, brilliant minds, lives devoted to medicine. Our society doesn't seem to attach very much kudos to those who work in the Health Service, but what could be more fundamental, more fulfilling, than helping sick people get better, or relieving people's suffering and enhancing the quality of life for those who have an incurable disease? What else is more important in a world where we have our priorities so mixed up?

Andrew was discharged on Monday 9th January and went to Broadgreen for his biopsy on the Tuesday which revealed a diagnosis of *High Grade, T-Cell, Lymphoblastic Non Hodgkins Lymphoma. According to the junior doctor on the ward, High Grade diseases where the abnormal cells divide quickly are generally more amenable to Chemotherapy, so I suppose this could be considered good news. However the rest of the diagnosis pointed to a very aggressive blood disease which, according to the counsellor, "would be very difficult to get on top of." However, we were really unaware of the full significance of Andrew's diagnosis at this stage of his illness and after only being admitted on the 4th January.

Andrew remained in hospital until 15th January when he was sufficiently well enough to come home for the day. By now the news of Andrew's illness had reached many people both in Ainsdale and in Durham and particularly the people of St John's, Ainsdale, which was to be the focus of a massive campaign of prayer for Andrew over the coming year. Andrew and myself started going to St John's in 1982 after joining the Christian Union at school in the same year. We were inspired by a young English teacher who not only ran the C.U., but was also involved in the youth work of the local Anglican church. We therefore decided it was time to join the church and partake in the youth activities, particularly the youth club on a Sunday evening which was known as the "Go-Club." It was the combined activities of the church, youth group and C.U. - holidays to Cornwall in 1983 and 1984 that did much to introduce us to a realistic and authentic Christian faith, which is based on a relationship with the living God, rather than a rule-keeping religion which involves regular church attendance. We were confirmed at St John's by the Bishop of Warrington in October 1983 and have continued to worship there up until we went to university in October 1988. However, we used to enjoy returning to the fellowship of St John's after our university terms. It is a typical Anglican church, with its middle of the road style of worship and often I wonder how much impact we are making on the people of Ainsdale, not to mention our financial problems which seem to go from bad to worse. However, despite these setbacks, which I suspect you would find in many churches these days, there is most importantly a fellowship of people with real love and concern for each other. This is the thing that matters most, as I suspect the Apostle Paul would have echoed in 1Corinthians 13. St John's is also privileged to have a very large youth group and it was the Young People in particular who showed an incredible amount of commitment and prayer for Andy in the months to come.

On Sunday 15th January I took Andrew to church for the 10:30 am Communion service. As we walked through the door and up the aisle it was the first time Andrew had been to church since he was diagnosed with cancer. He had lost weight, looked jaundiced and was generally weaker than his normal self. There was a tangible sign of love and concern by the congregation especially when I accompanied Andrew to the altar rail to receive communion. It was a very emotional occasion for me. We were exposing Andrew's illness to the people of Ainsdale and I was unsure how people would react. At the end of the service, our Lay Reader, Angela Evans showed real commitment and came over to pray with Andrew and there were several of us who prayed for him with the laying on of hands for healing. It was a public symbol of commitment and it broke me and I couldn't control my emotions. Looking back on it, I suppose it was very funny because I was in floods of tears and Andy was laughing and joking and telling me to pull myself together! We had launched a massive campaign of prayer which eventually led to 32 weekly newsletters circulated to the congregation and 25 people throughout the country (Over 800 individual newsletters in people's hands). An evening prayer meeting at church which lasted for half an hour from 9:00 - 9:30pm and which lasted from mid-February (each day) up until Andrew's death in October (where it was being held on a Monday, Wednesday & Friday). This was the vital lifeline which sustained Andrew in his battle with Lymphoma. It was not prayer with defeatism or the easy way out prayers like "your will be done" - it was fervent, positive and courageous prayer asking God to do great things and it works!

Despite several regimes which had been debated and discarded, Tuesday 24th January arrived and it was Day 1 of chemotherapy. In some ways we had all been preparing for this day, and we were all aware that without treatment, Andrew's disease would become uncontrollable. A Hickman Catheter had been inserted the week before and a chemotherapy protocol called UKALL 12 had eventually been decided on. This is a clinical trial for Acute Lymphoblastic Leukaemia. The aim of Phase I and Phase II would be to achieve a remission. Phase I involved a four week cocktail of drugs which included Prednisolone (a steroid which is taken orally), Vincristine (taken once a week for four weeks by intravenous injection), Daunorubicin (administered once a week for four weeks by *intravenous infusion), and finally L'Asparaginese which was administered by *sub-cutaneous injection over 12 days. One of the symptoms of Andrew's disease was fluid in the pleural cavity. This pleural effusion would provide a clue to the success of the phase of Andrew's chemotherapy.

We had already been warned of the possible side effects:- Nausea, Vomiting, Hairloss, diahorrea, Constipation, Life-threatening infections; it seemed like a never ending list of bad news! But again, me and Andy would joke, "If it isn't hurting, it isn't working" stealing John Major's well publicised phrase about the economy and applying it to his treatment.

Andrew was upset on the Monday night before chemotherapy began on the Tuesday. He, as a chemist, was well aware that the drugs he was about to have were deadly toxic and the realisation that the real battle was about to begin had brought fear. I was with Andy on Tuesday 24th January when the nurse put up his first bag of cytotoxic drugs. The next 4 weeks were going to be very crucial.

CHAPTER FOUR

A BLACK WEEK AT HALF TERM

HALF TERM, February 1995 was supposed to be a well deserved break from school and a chance to spend more time with Andrew. It turned out to be the most harrowing week of my life as Andrew's life held in the balance. It also prompted a massive commitment to prayer which brought about a miracle of God's grace which we will always be grateful for.

Despite four weeks of intensive chemotherapy, Andrew's fluid on his lungs (pleural effusion) kept coming back and it was becoming clear that things were certainly not going to plan. Despite our hopes and prayers, Andrew was becoming increasingly debilitated and he had to have his Hickman line removed on 15th February due to a deep vein thrombosis or clot in his *superior vena cava (SVC) which had caused his arms and feet to swell up. He had speckled red marks across his chest due to low platelet count and was losing weight rapidly, but this was just the tip of the iceberg. A sore throat had meant that Andrew had been put on diamorphine in order to ease the pain and he was showing a fluctuating temperature which is usually a sign of infection. On the Sunday 19th February the Chaplain came to give Andrew, my friend Emma and myself Holy Communion for his first time in hospital. I remember him walking gingerly to the toilet with massively swollen feet and using his drip stand to help him balance. He seemed so fragile and weak. Little did I know that it would be the last time he would walk for months. The Chaplain, a coloured gentleman called Sam Pratt, was an excellent support and a man full of joy and faith. He gave us hope and helped us to focus on Jesus and be positive that God was going to get Andrew through this difficult time and "on the road to recovery" as he used to say.

So half term came and the consultant Dr Chu came round on the Monday afternoon to see Andrew. He didn't really say very much apart from the fact they were changing Andrew's antibiotics and they were going to give Andrew an injection called *GCSF in order to help his white blood cells (neutrophils) come back to fight his infection. Speaking to him in the corridor and later with Mrs Cook the counsellor, the picture was starting to get darker and darker. They were disappointed with the chemotherapy and although they did not give up lightly Andrew had "a tremendously hard battle on his hands." My heart was starting to sink and I was starting to get frightened. Everything seemed to be going wrong. Our prayers seemed to be falling on deaf ears but I said in the doctors office that we would just have to pray harder. (I could see the looks of astonishment and I feel somewhat embarrassed about it now!)

I had to keep people at church informed because the nightly prayer meetings were becoming the only source of hope in these difficult days. On the Monday night I arrived at church to meet a group of around 20 people. God works in wonderful ways because throughout Andrew's illness we were constantly amazed by the huge commitment to pray. I managed to give an up to date account of Andrew's condition and inform people that we were praying for Andrew's white blood cells to come back and his *pleural effusion to subside. I arrived back at my flat in Birkdale when Geoff my landlord told me that the doctor had been on the phone asking if I could ring her as Andrew was having difficulty getting to sleep and was getting frightened. Geoff drove me down to the hospital and arrived just before midnight. I spoke to Michelle, the staff nurse, who made me up a bed next to Andrew's in Ward 9. I remember overhearing a conversation with her and a nurse who was coming on to the night shift, "We have a fight on with Andy." As Monday night drifted into Tuesday, Andrew was becoming increasingly agitated and had a temperature of 40.5°c. His condition was deteriorating. We had to keep praying but as Mum said, "You had better ask your friends for a miracle now."

CHAPTER FIVE

PEOPLE IN PRAYER

ON **WEDNESDAY** morning we were called at home early, at around 6.00am. Andrew had had a very disturbing night and he was frightened of going back to sleep. He was asking for his brother. We drove to Liverpool and arrived at about 6:30am to be met by the temporary Chaplain who had been keeping a vigil by Andrew's bed. It was clear that Andrew's high temperature during the night had been causing him to hallucinate and have very vivid nightmares. He wasn't totally coherent, but he kept waving his hands in the air saying, "Thank you Jesus, Thank You Jesus." He was very agitated and I was frightened that he would fall out of bed. I decided the first thing I should do was find Andy's Bible and read a suitable passage of scripture before praying for Andy.

In situations of difficulty it is amazing how you can find a passage which just speaks so much into a situation. The words of Ephesians chapter 6 about standing against the evil one were illuminating:

Put on all of God's armour so that you will be able to stand safe against the strategies and tricks of Satan. For we are not fighting against people made of flesh and blood, but against persons without bodies - the evil rulers of the unseen world, those mighty satanic beings and great evil princes of darkness who rule this world; and against huge numbers of wicked spirits in the spirit world. So use every piece of God's armour to resist the enemy whenever he attacks and when it is all over, you will still be standing up.

(Eph 6 v11-13 Living Bible Edition)

It sounds rather dramatic, but when you have been screaming and shouting in the middle of the night and needed three nurses to come and sit with you to calm you down, when you are dreaming you can see a coffin in the front room of your own home, when the Devil is pulling you one way, and your Vicar from Durham, Michael Wilcock, is hanging onto you and pulling you back. When everything is vivid and you actually think you are dying, it's not surprising that a passage like Ephesians suddenly seems incredibly real and pertinent to the situation you are in.

As our Vicar Tony had said when he came to visit Andrew on the Tuesday, not being frightened is crucial, because the fear accompanied with serious illness can be just as crippling as the illness itself. The church was proving to be very supportive, particularly that week. Tony and Una had been to see Andrew on the Tuesday to give him prayer and encouragement not to give up. The PCC had stood at the end of their meeting on the Tuesday night as the news of the seriousness of Andrew's illness had begun to reach the congregation, in silent prayer for Andrew. The nightly prayer meetings were beginning to attract up to 20-25 people as the urgency of the situation started to reach home. Other churches also started to pray.

It was Wednesday 22nd February 1995. Andrew was extremely ill with a high temperature (40°c) and he was becoming increasingly weak and debilitated. Mum and I had been sitting by his bed all morning and into the afternoon. Mum had just taken a break to go to the toilet when Andrew looked at me and said in a weak voice, "Please Mike, Look after Mum and Dad." We went into the doctor's office at about 4:00pm whilst Andrew was sleeping. Dr Caswell, the Senior Registrar, was there and Mum and I wanted to know what was going on, we could see with our own eyes that Andrew was deteriorating. His reply was silencing and it is a moment that is etched forever on my mind:-

"I'm afraid that Andrew has a very very serious infection and the outlook is very very grim."

There was little more one could say. The infection was a *fungal septicaemia and this is basically a blood infection, equivalent to blood poisoning. They were about to start Andrew on a drug called *Amphotericin. It is an anti-fungal drug with toxic side effects, making the kidney's lose potassium, so he would need to be carefully monitored and given regular intravenous potassium supplements. There were no guarantees, the only comfort Dr Caswell could give us was to reassure us:-

"We are doing everything we can."

We walked out of the office, almost stunned by the news. I remember Mum saying, "You can't get more honest than that can you!"

We decided to go home, tell everyone the news and have a quick tea and then come back straight away, as they were going to put a line in Andrew's neck in order to administer the new drugs. We said goodbye to Andrew, he was suitably courageous as he whispered to me:-

"I'm not giving up........ I'm going to keep on fighting"

I told him we just couldn't give up, but he had no idea that we had just been in to see the doctors and that I knew full well what an almighty battle we had on our hands.

We drove home from Liverpool on a dull, wet and drizzly Wednesday afternoon. Hardly a word was uttered as we drove the thirty-five minute journey back to Ainsdale. I was very close to tears, but there was no time for crying; we had to be strong and keep supporting each other. We walked in and Dad was waiting for us. We went into the front room and my Mum said:-

"Bill, they don't think he's going to make it."

I have never, ever, in my life seen my Dad cry until that day when he just broke down and we all held each other in the front room. It was a terribly emotional time and the strain of the last two months was starting to show, even with someone who usually kept his emotions to himself.

Next we rang Burnley and my Mum's youngest sister Auntie Linda came over straight away. Again more tears as we explained what Dr Caswell had said. We would have to ring Natalie in Scotland as we had asked if she should come down and the doctor had thought it was best if she was to come home. All the time we were planning. Mum made the tea, we decided who would stay at the hospital and who would come home. We set off again and we were desperately thinking of what we would say to Andrew about Auntie Linda being with us, as we didn't want him to be unduly alarmed.

As we went up in the lift to Ward 7Y I could feel the determination and faith beginning to well up inside. This was going to be a fight and God was on our side. There were so many people praying and rooting for Andrew. It wasn't the time for Andrew to die, and I just couldn't entertain that terrible thought so soon into his illness. We were ready to fight and God's will would be done.

They had moved Andrew into a side room and fitted a *Central Venous Catheter (CVC) into a vein in his neck whilst we had been gone. Apparently Andrew had asked the doctor "Does this mean I am going to die?" as they were moving him into a room on his own. A yellow bag of Amphotericin was about to go up. This would be the key to getting on top of Andrew's infection, but would his white cells come back in order to fight his infection naturally? All we could do was pray. We needed a miracle!

CHAPTER SIX

HOPE IN THE DARKNESS

IT WAS WEDNESDAY evening at 7Y. Andrew was in the side room and the first bag of a yellow looking drug called Amphotericin was up on the drip stand. He had been running a temperature of 40.5°c earlier that day so we were hoping for an immediate response to the treatment.

It was 9:00pm - the time when I knew that in Ainsdale a faithful group of people would be gathering to pray. I went down to the Chapel with Dad and we sat and I prayed and pleaded with God to spare Andrew's life. One of the Psalms spoke very clearly to me as I prayed. It was Psalm 116:-

I love the Lord because he hears my prayers and answers them. Because he bends down and listens, I will pray as long as I breathe!" Death stared me in the face, I was frightened and sad. Then I cried, "Lord, save me!" How kind he is, how good he is! So merciful this God of ours! The Lord protects the simple and child-like. I was facing death and then he saved me. Now I can relax. For the Lord has done this wonderful miracle for me. He has saved me from death, my eyes from tears, my feet from stumbling. I shall live! Yes, in his presence, here on earth!

In my discouragement I thought "They are lying when they say I will recover....... But now what can I offer Jehovah for all he has done for me? (Ps 116 v1-12 Living Bible Edn)

If that was not a word from God for the situation I was in then what is!! But it was verse 15 which leapt from the page and spoke to me directly:-

His loved ones are very precious to him and he does not lightly let them die. (Ps 116 v15)"

There was a promise from God which I kept reading out aloud, again and again in the Chapel, tears beginning to roll down my face as I knelt down by the altar rail. Andrew was very precious to God because he was one of his children and God would not let him die lightly. God had spoken to me and I believed from that moment that Andrew would not die in vain and that perhaps he would get a second chance of life and more treatment. It was one of the few moments I have had in my Christian life when I actually felt God had spoken to me in that verse and what a wonderful verse it was.

Things were beginning to change. I was not feeling as desperate and dispirited as I had been earlier on in the day. My emotions were prone to sudden swings but now was the time to pray hard, have deep faith in God and support Andy as much as was humanly possible. The medical team were doing everything possible to save him and he was in excellent hands. Thursday was the ward round and Dr Chu would no doubt give us an up to date position.

Andrew had a relatively comfortable night and there was a dramatic response to his first dose of Amphotericin as his temperature dropped down to about 36.9°c. The temperature chart was starting to look like a series of mountain peaks by now! On Thursday morning he was catheterised in order to keep a record of his fluid intake and out-take and to make him feel more comfortable. He had a blood transfusion and was due to see Dr Chu in the afternoon. We had some hilarious moments that day which involved Andrew making private calls on the phone which was one of the special privileges of being in a side room. At one point, when he was just about to speak to his friend Patrick Steel in Durham, he announced to Mum, Dad, Natalie & Tony, "This is a private conversation - do you mind leaving the room!" He was so poorly and yet the way he spoke on the phone was entirely normal; you wouldn't have believed this was a critically ill patient, who was at death's door.

Dr Chu came round in the afternoon and sat by Andrew's bed. He told Andrew that they were carrying on with his Amphotericin and GCSF treatment and he folded Andrew's chemotherapy chart up and said he would not be having anymore chemotherapy for the moment. Apparently, Andrew gave him a good cross examination because every time Dr Chu stood up to leave he would ask him another question and he would sit down again! We were still awaiting news of Andrew's *neutrophil count which was critical as to whether he would be able to fight off his infection.

Friday came and we were still praying that Andrew's white cell count would come back to fight his infection. Andrew had a swollen stomach with some wonderful coloured speckles all over it. Dr Caswell said, "Oh I haven't seen this before." They appeared to be something of a novelty being a red wine colour and everyone was taking an interest. Andrew's temperature was starting to come down to more reasonable levels at 37°C, and he had a *platelet transfusion because his platelet count was low which makes you susceptible to bleeding and bruising as the platelets help the blood to clot.

Andrew had not left his bed since Sunday 19th February. He had become increasingly weaker and debilitated and his body ached because he had been lying in bed so long. It was frightening to see the nurses having to move him in order to allow him to go to the toilet or change the sheets on his bed. He was also having to be turned from side to side in order to prevent sores developing on his back and bottom. When you see someone so helpless and weak, when you remember them not so long ago being able to run and walk and dance and not get tired easily, it is frightening to think you can lose the things you take for granted so quickly and become dependent on others for your survival. This unfortunately was the nature of the disease that Andrew had contracted, and a serious infection on top of his cancer which was not under control were leading to his general debilitation. Fortunately he had excellent nursing care. Lynn, Cilla and Rachel on the side ward were wonderful with him, cleaning his bed, helping him to move from side to side, giving him bed washes, helping him to "Keep your kecks on Andy. OOPS! He's lost his kecks again!" Such efficient and careful nursing was a tremendous help to Andrew. They had even given him a special Pegasus Air mattress which responds to the slightest movement in order to prevent him getting serious bed sores.

A new type of Amphotericin which is less toxic on the kidneys and more soluble was introduced on the Friday afternoon. This *ABLC or *Lipid Complex of Amphotericin is less toxic to the body and therefore more efficient and safer at fighting infection but it was also very expensive. Finally the doctors had ordered a more effective growth factor called *GMCSF but this had to be ordered and would take a few days to arrive. We got the impression that everything possible that could be done by the medical experts was being done to save Andrew from the septicaemia. There seemed to be a glimmer of hope in the darkness but his condition was still critical. I kept reminding myself as I sat at the end of his bed in this little side room of the scripture that had meant so much to me on Wednesday evening

His loved ones are very precious to him and he does not lightly let them die. (Ps 116v15).

Would the God I believed in hear all our cries and prayers?

CHAPTER SEVEN

GOD OF MIRACLES

IT WAS SATURDAY morning the 25th February 1995. Andrew had had a reasonable night but he had been calling out during the night and had been given some sleeping tablets to help him sleep. He was still critically ill and we awaited news of his response to the hormone injection which were supposed to generate the recovery of his infection fighting white blood cells.

The Doctor on weekend call was Dr Edwin Lee, a registrar specialising in Haematology. They kept Andrew's temperature and blood pressure record outside his side room and I remember Dr Lee studying these charts outside his room. Although Andrew's temperature was still fluctuating it was at a lower level since he had commenced amphotericin. His blood results had also come through.

Dr Lee went to see Andrew looking very excited!

"Fingers crossed Andrew, I think we turn a corner!"

Andrew's neutrophil count was up to 13.9! The GCSF treatment had done its job in stimulating the growth of new cells. With Andrew's natural means of defence starting to work, he might possibly recover from his septicaemia after all. We had prayed that Andrew's white cell count would recover ever since the Wednesday night at the nightly prayer meeting. At last we had a small bit of good news and the doctor at least seemed very encouraged. When he looked at the temperature chart I also heard him remark, "This shows a dramatic response to Amphotericin." It was time to encourage Andrew with this "guarded optimism" but Andrew didn't seem very impressed.

The fact that he had been on sleeping tablets meant that he wasn't 100% as you might say!

"That doctor's a liar!" he exclaimed, much to everybody's surprise, but Cilla, the nurse who was on the side ward that morning was reassuring:-

"No Andrew, he wouldn't lie to you!"

Andrew was given the new GMCSF injection on the Saturday morning. However in the afternoon he had started to get frightened and he had been reaching for his Bible whilst half asleep and calling for 'Michael'. My sister Natalie who had been sitting by his bedside was upset by this and Andrew appeared to be unconvinced that his condition was improving. Talking to the nurses on the Saturday evening, they were also not as optimistic as the doctor had been that morning. Even if he had a 13.9 neutrophil count, these were only "baby" cells and would take a while to mature. Freda took Andrew's temperature in the evening and he was only registering 36.9°C and yet he was so clammy and his pyjamas were drenched with sweat. As she explained, sometimes the disease can actually make the patient feel a lot warmer than a thermometer would pick up. This was the main problem. Andrew, without more chemotherapy, would have an uncontrollable disease and yet chemotherapy would not be considered as an option until his infection had abated and his overall condition had improved. We were stuck in a difficult position.

Mum and I both decided to keep a vigil by his bedside that evening. The time seemed so precious that neither of us wanted to leave Andrew that evening. We were getting differing opinions about the true nature of his condition within the space of a few hours and this was getting me a little bit frustrated.

My friend Steve rang and he had come up with a novel idea. As well as having the evening prayer meetings, why not start writing a weekly newsletter which could be produced every Saturday, typed up and then photocopied and handed out to the congregation at the Sunday morning service. It sounded an excellent idea and so we discussed what needed to go in and later he rang me back to read out the completed version. The first newsletter "Andy Ridge" went out on Sunday 26th February. They were left at the back of the church but had all disappeared by the end of the service. As far as I was concerned, the more we made people aware of Andrew's illness and the more people prayed the better it would be!

As we sat and looked at Andrew sleeping in his bed, my Mum showed me a letter he had written to her when he had been terribly homesick at Oxford University in October 1988. She kept it in a small compartment in her handbag because it was a beautiful letter from a son to his mother saying how much he appreciated the fact that she was always there to talk to him. It made me cry. Seven years on, here we were in a tiny side ward in Liverpool with Andrew fighting for his life. How life had changed so much and how uncertain life could be!

We had to stay positive. As I had prayed for Andrew that evening I had read the words of Romans 8 about "nothing being able to separate us from the love of Christ" and I had quietly read Psalm 23 to Andrew before he dosed off to sleep:

Because the Lord is my shepherd, I have everything I need! He lets me rest in the meadow grass and leads me beside the quiet streams. He restores my failing health. He helps me to do what honours him the most. (Psalm 23 v 1-3 Living Bible Edn)

Ann Cook, the Haematology Counsellor, came in late on Saturday evening and came into the side room to see how Andrew was. A Christian lady, I was finding it increasingly easier to talk to her and find out what was happening. She had arranged for the Rev. Alan Godson to come in and give me and Andrew Holy Communion on Sunday afternoon which would be an extra encouragement. I remember her telling me that evening "The disease is rampant" which was soul destroying but at least she was being honest and we knew exactly how grave the situation was.

There was the constant buzzing of the drip as Andrew's antibiotics went through during the night. On Sunday morning I went home to go to church and found myself feeling doubtful as to whether Andrew was going to get better. We stayed behind and a group of us prayed because I had said, "I'm not sure he's going to make it." As we finished praying, someone came in with a message from the vicar's wife Una, "Andrew's condition has improved a little this morning." There was still hope, we just had to keep praying and never give up. I had begun to let doubt creep into my mind but I had to trust God absolutely that he would get Andrew through this infection and he would be able to have some more chemotherapy.

The Rev. Alan Godson was a breath of fresh air. I could see that this rather eccentric man was indeed a man of God, and not only that, he had twin sons so he could empathise even more with the situation we were in. He talked to Andrew and me about his mother who had died a Christian at a ripe old age and how he had had a serious illness a few years ago and was disappointed when he realised he had come back to planet earth again instead of being with Christ in glory. I could see what he was doing. He was trying to help us to see death was something not to be feared, but a wonderful thing to go and be with Jesus. We all gave each other communion and then he asked if he could pray for us. Andrew replied, "Please pray for me." So we gathered around each other and prayed, "Oh God you are so powerful....We know that you could heal Andrew right now if you wanted to....." he began. He asked God to give us strength to get through this situation and that His will would be done in both of our lives. This man had such an infectious and real faith we felt really comforted and ministered to. However he hadn't finished! He wanted to meet Mum and Dad and Auntie Linda! In the day room he gathered them all into a rugby scrum kind of formation and prayed for all of us and for Andrew. You should have seen the look on the faces of some of the visitors in the day room! I'll bet they were wondering, "What is that bunch of lunatics doing over there in a circle?"

Then Alan Godson said his goodbyes and we were left feeling encouraged and somewhat surprised by this rather unorthodox vicar who was obviously not embarrassed about his faith in the slightest.

By Monday morning Andrew's neutrophils were 15.1 and although he was complaining about being very tired he was drinking and starting to eat solid food again. His temperature was beginning to fall and the Amphotericin was obviously helping to fight his infection. By the time his new consultant, Professor Cawley, came to see Andrew on Thursday afternoon the 2nd March, he was back on the main ward and they were talking about chemotherapy recommencing in two weeks' time. His septicaemia had been brought under control and the worst was over. I spoke to the junior doctor that Tuesday evening. "He is a very lucky man, most people would have died from what he's just had." We had asked for a miracle and God had kept the promise of his word. "His loved ones are very precious to him and he does not lightly let them die."

CHAPTER EIGHT

CARRYING ON

PROFESSOR CAWLEY was the senior consultant on Ward 7Y and a haematologist whose specialised in white cell disorders. He was a pleasantly spoken man who appeared to be a typical academic but very approachable and made Andrew's family feel a part of the discussions when he came on ward round. He met Andrew for the first time on Thursday 2nd March. I remember the occasion very well. He came and sat down in the chair next to Andrew's bed and said:

"Hello Andrew, I've heard a lot about you, you've been having quite a rough time from what I hear."

to which Andrew's magnanimous response was something along the lines of "Yes.... Just a bit!" The Professor was very keen to ask Andrew what he felt his needs were at the moment to which Andrew replied that he was tired of people going on about his eating and drinking and he was finding it hard to eat because often he had no appetite. The Professor reassured him about this and told him that he should just eat and drink what he could and not worry too much. Unfortunately, weight loss was to be a major problem as Andrew's weight plummeted from 9 stone 3lb (59Kg) on 6th February to 7 stone (44.6Kg) on 21st March and this led to Andrew eventually being put on *Total Parenteral Nutrition (T.P.N.) liquid nutrition in order to prevent his further deterioration.

The Professor explained that they would keep Andrew on Amphotericin for another week in order to clear up his infection and then they would proceed with Phase II of the chemotherapy protocol which would be a new assortment of drugs in about two weeks time. However, because Andrew's response to Phase I of UKALL12 had been disappointing and he still had fluid on his lungs there was a need to get on with further treatment as soon as was humanly possible without putting Andrew in a life threatening situation. As the junior doctor had told me in the office:

"I'm pushing for further chemotherapy.....as Andrew is already in a poorer prognostic group."

So chemotherapy was due to start again on Friday 17th March but it actually commenced on the 10th, a week earlier than had first been talked about.

Things however did not go so smoothly between the 2nd and the 10th March. On the Monday night Andrew lost a large amount of blood through his bowels and he was placed on a Critical Care Protocol. His blood pressure had dropped and this was being monitored every hour. He was being carefully nursed and platelets and clotting factors had been given in order to prevent further loss of blood. As we walked into Ward 7Y on Monday evening, the Professor was on his way out, but he stopped to reassure us:-

"I feel the team are following all the right procedures."

Speaking to Dr Ledson later on that Monday evening the situation was very serious:-

"We are pushing very hard up hill at the moment and this is just another added complication. If Andrew didn't respond to his transfusions and clotting factors it may be a question of allowing him to have a peaceful death."

It was time to pray and ask for a new intervention from God. As I sat at Andrew's bedside on that Monday evening, I was desperately trying to think of a Bible passage which would be appropriate to the situation he was in. Then I had a sudden inspiration. What about the story of Jesus healing the lady who had been subject to bleeding for twelve years. I opened my Bible and the first page open was Matthew chapter 9. There it was right in front of my eyes!:-

As Jesus and the disciples were going to the Rabbi's home a woman who had been ill for twelve years with internal bleeding came up behind him and touched a tassel of his robe, for she thought "If I only touch Him, I will be healed" Jesus turned around and spoke to her. "Daughter," he said, "all is well! Your faith has healed you." And the woman was well from that moment. (Matthew 9 v19-22)

If you don't believe that God doesn't still speak to us today through his word, believe me he does! As I read this God-given passage with real conviction, I prayed that Andrew's bleeding would cease and the medical interventions would be successful.

By the Tuesday the amount of bleeding coming from Andrew's bowels had been reduced and by Wednesday Andrew's medical notes reported no *Melaena or blood in his diahorrea. Another hurdle had been successfully negotiated and it was time to press on with more chemotherapy.

Phase II of Andrew's chemotherapy consisted of a cocktail of four drugs which were used in the treatment of Acute Lymphoblastic Leukaemia. Cyclophosphamide was administered every fortnight by intravenous infusion, Cytarabine (Ara-C) was administered every week over four days by intravenous infusion. 6 Mercaptopurine were administered daily in tablet form and Methotrexate was administered *intrathecally once every week. This last drug was given in the form of a *lumbar puncture, which is an injection into the *Cerebro-Spinal Fluid (CSF) through the base of the spine. Andrew found these rather uncomfortable but fortunately he only had three out of the full course of five. Because Andrew's Hickman line had had to be removed because it had caused a thrombosis, he had a line put into his neck in order to have the chemotherapy. These lines had to be replaced periodically because they were prone to infection, which was the last thing Andrew needed. On one occasion he had a temperature of 38.6°C which was worrying because it could mean an infection would halt the progress of his chemotherapy. A new line was put in that afternoon and by the evening his temperature was back to the normal therapeutic range of 36.5°C.

Andrew and I were well aware of the importance of Phase II of the chemotherapy. He still had fluid on his lungs and we needed a positive response to the 4 new drugs that were being given. Our third Prayer Newsletter also informed the people at St John's how important it was:-

"The main point for prayer will be the success of the next phase of Andrew's chemotherapy. Please pray that it will be a major step forward for him and that he has no more infections or setbacks!"

The medical team did not seem as optimistic. Mrs Cook had spoken to Mum when she had been sitting in Andrew's side ward watching him sleep on Friday morning. Apparently Mum had asked if anyone on the ward ever got better, to which the reply had been somewhat sobering:-

"A few, not many. But Andrew has a very aggressive disease which will be very difficult to get on top of."

There was no point in our building false hopes or expecting Andrew to be suddenly better from such a serious illness. However, we had to be positive and determined to carry on as otherwise he might as well just give up, curl up and wait to die. Getting this balance between optimism and realism is very difficult, especially when your emotions were involved. However, we were grateful that the medical team were being so honest with us, even though the long-term outlook was gloomy. I was reminded of the bible verse which was stuck on the wall above Andrew's bed:

For with God, ALL things are possible   (Mark 10 v27)

On Monday 20th March I arrived at the hospital to be greeted with some good news. After two weeks of Phase II chemotherapy, the fluid on Andrew's lungs had all but disappeared on the latest X-ray. This meant that he was responding to the chemotherapy and his malignant cells were beginning to be killed off in greater quantities. Dr Ledson the SHO, even brought Andrew the x-rays to show the difference and how the first x-ray had fluid but on the second x-ray it had all but disappeared. It was good to encourage him and actually let him see the evidence for himself because he was starting to get a little depressed and frustrated. He had been confined to a bed in a tiny side room for nearly 4 weeks. He hadn't been out into the fresh air since 11th February. No wonder he was feeling depressed! At last we had the real first piece of positive news for nearly 3 months and I was full of happiness as I left the ward that night. We held a Prayer and Praise meeting at church to thank God for all his faithfulness to us on the Friday evening. He had brought Andrew through a terribly difficult time and our prayers as well as the medical expertise were at last bearing some fruit. Here was a tired young man, all seven stone of him, battling to stay alive. We had a long way to go but as winter gave way to spring and the nights started to get lighter there was a glimmer of hope and a bit of a respite from those dark days of January and February. There were signs of new life in the flowers and trees and there was the new life and second chance Andrew had been given and it was vital and so precious to us all.

CHAPTER NINE

NO SIGN OF DISEASE

O**N MONDAY** 27th March Professor Cawley and Dr Caswell came to tell Andrew that they were going to recommend a break from his chemotherapy and he was moved back onto the main ward the following day. Andrew and I used to joke because by now he had been in Room 6, Room 7, Room 9, and two different side rooms, so if he ended up in Room 8 he would have completed a full tour of the ward! He had completed around 75% of Phase II of his treatment but any more chemotherapy could have killed him. He was still very weak and confined to his bed and receiving Total Parenteral Nutrition in order to help stabilise his weight. For the next two weeks Andrew suffered from bleeding from his bowels and had to have daily transfusions of platelets and blood in order to help his blood clot and restore blood which had been lost. He had thirty-six bags of platelets in the space of seven days. By the time this bleeding had finally stopped, he had started to show a fluctuating temperature and there was a shadow on his chest X-ray that indicated he had a chest infection. The Professor came round on the Thursday to tell Andrew that his fungal infection would be treated with ABLC and that 'now was the right time' to start his GCSF treatment in order to boost his white cell count which would help to fight his infection. Last time Andrew had had an infection and GCSF, had been back in February and it was very serious. Mrs Cook, the Haematology Counsellor, reassured me that this wasn't as serious as the septicaemia he had had previously. We had also discussed the possibility of taking Andrew out for a trip in the car as we were now starting the Easter Holidays (13th April) and Andrew hadn't seen the outside world since 11th February. Although he could not stand or even walk, he could be lifted into a wheelchair and then he could be more mobile. The main difficulty would be lifting him from the wheelchair into the passenger seat of the car. Mum and I were not trained to lift Andrew properly although we had been helping him move around his bed, and I had helped him onto the commode a couple of times and so we didn't think this would be a problem. We had to get Andrew out of the hospital - even just for a couple of hours for a drive over to the Wirral because he desperately needed a break. The Professor and Mrs Cook both agreed with us and thought it was a feasible idea. Andrew's antibiotics only took four hours so he could have them in the morning and then be disconnected from his drip in the afternoon. The nurse was a bit more sceptical and asked what happens if he has any more diahorrea or Melaena? (At this time he had been frequently on the toilet). It was important to cover all eventualities but I was determined Andrew must go so we said we would take bed pans, urine bottles and the rest of the necessary equipment with us. Permission was granted and Easter Saturday was to be his first glimpse of life outside hospital for sixty-three days. You can't even begin to imagine what it must have been like for him to be so restricted and trapped in hospital for so long.

We all were looking forward to Saturday afternoon because earlier on in the year we had really wondered whether he would see the outside world again having been so desperately ill.

When Saturday afternoon came, we enlisted the help of 'Big Andy', the staff nurse, as we took Andrew down to the side entrance in a wheelchair with a blanket over him to keep him warm. We pulled the wheelchair up at the passenger side of the car and in one swift move Andy lifted him right out of the wheelchair, swung him round and placed him in the passenger seat, and I quickly ran round to help lift his legs and feet into a comfortable position. Success! We had got him into the car and set off through the Mersey Tunnel to the Wirral, which is a peninsula to the west of Liverpool that we often went to as teenagers. It was a cool, windy day but despite some scattered clouds there was brilliant Spring sunshine. We passed through the tunnel and made our way to Parkgate via the hills which overlook the Wirral estuary. I was sitting in the back of the car and I vividly remember watching Andrew as his head turned slowly to the left and he gazed out at the landscape, Liverpool and the Mersey estuary in the distance; you could see the look of excitement on his face as he gazed out and the Spring sunshine reflected off the windows of the car. His face looked like he had forgotten what the outside world was like as though he was marvelling at this beautiful place he hadn't seen for so long. It brought tears to my eyes and I thanked God for allowing Andrew to see this wonderful Spring day with all the evidence of new life on view. It was a day that Andrew could so easily never have lived to see and we were so grateful he had survived those dark days of January and February. By the time we had celebrated Easter with coffee and hot cross buns at Parkgate promenade it was time to drive back to the Royal and we got home at 5:00pm. Andrew was exhausted and he was back in the nick of time because he was in desperate need of the commode! This was followed by the delights of Saturday evening meal, Chicken curry! In that short journey of three hours' duration Andrew had seen God's world again and appreciated what a precious gift it was to be alive. He took all of Easter Sunday to recover and his legs were aching tremendously but he was much encouraged by an enormous card from St John's to wish him a Happy Easter, which had been signed by many in the congregation, as well as a large Thorntons Easter Egg to help him maintain his nutritional status as Dr Chu would have said!

By the end of April, Andrew's blood counts had risen and he was being treated for a fungal infection on his chest. He was slowly becoming more mobile but the weakness in his legs was causing concern and this would have to be investigated. He had little sensation in his feet which were stone cold compared to the rest of his body and his legs had lost a great deal of muscle which made Mum describe him to the consultant on one occasion as "a bag of bones!"

Despite this there was some very encouraging news. Andrew had a *Bone Marrow Aspirate and C.T. Scan on the 5th May to reassess his response to his treatment. The CT Scan revealed "no active sign of disease" and the bone marrow films which had been examined by the haematologists reported "...the presence of mature neutrophils. No blasts were seen." I spoke to the nurse on the Monday and she told me that Andy was much better than he had been and the haematologists were pleased with his bone marrow results. With this pleasing news it was time to concentrate on helping Andrew to get back on his feet. Although he was having half an hour's physiotherapy a day this was clearly not going to be enough and the main emphasis had to be on rehabilitation and giving Andrew's body time to recover from the battering it had received. He needed to walk again.

By now Andrew was on his third consultant. Dr Clark was a tall man, with a more formal approach to the ward round. He was going to arrange an *MRI Scan (Magnetic Resonance Imaging) and some other nerve conductivity tests in order to investigate the weakness in Andrew's legs. The next goal would be for him to make a visit home and it was time to encourage him. So many of our prayers had been answered and he was making progress.

CHAPTER TEN

REHABILITATION

ANDREW'S MRI Scan on his lumbar spine revealed nothing untoward but the tests on his nerves which were done after referring him to the Consultant neurologist revealed severe damage to Andrew's nerve endings in his arms and feet. This permanent *peripheral neuropathy in his feet meant he might never be able to regain full sensation and be able to move the lower part of his foot and toes. It was decided by the medical team on the 11th May that Andrew should be referred to a Youth Rehabilitation Centre at either Broadgreen or Fazakerley hospitals which could provide him with the intensive physiotherapy he needed in order to get back on his feet and get him walking again.

On the 13th May we celebrated another milestone. Andrew was granted afternoon leave and so we drove the thirty-five minute journey home and surprised Mum and Dad. It was the figuring out of how to get the wheelchair into the house which caused the greatest amusement! Andrew spent four hours at home, it was the first time he had been back home for over three months and several of his friends came round to say hello and congratulate him on being back in Ainsdale!

The weekend after Andrew was sufficiently well enough to come home and watch the Cup Final with his father, and it was even better when Everton duly provided the magic by beating Manchester United 1 goal to nil.

All the time Andrew was slowly getting stronger and he was able to do arm exercises with weights to strengthen his arm muscles. His legs however, were hopelessly behind and would take a long time to build up any muscle mass and get his legs as straight as possible. The Professor and Dr Clark had apparently "never seen such muscle wastage" as with Andrew's legs.

We prayed that Andrew's referral to a Rehabilitation Centre would be a swift one and we were not disappointed. By the end of May, Andrew had been accepted by the Younger Disabled Unit at Fazakerley as an ideal candidate. We were pleased with this choice. Broadgreen had the advantage of being in touch with Dr Chu who did a clinic there once a week, which meant he would have been able to keep a personal eye on him. However, for Andrew's family, Fazakerley hospital was nearer home and far easier to get to than Broadgreen, and so we were pleased that he had been accepted. All that had to happen now was Andrew had to be weaned off his intravenous medication so his line could be taken out and then it was literally waiting for a suitable day to leave.

On 31st May Andrew ended his ten week course of Total Parenteral Nutrition. Seventy days of liquid food had helped him stabilise his weight but it was now time to start eating normally and he would have to make a special effort. He also started what was described as "maintenance" chemotherapy which consisted of taking a tablet called 6-Mercaptopurine daily, the idea of this being to keep on top of his disease whilst he was away for an interim period before he would have further aggressive treatment back at the Royal.

On the 4th June Andrew managed to go to church at St John's Ainsdale after six months in hospital. The last time he had been in church was on the 15th January not long after being initially diagnosed. This time there was one major difference. Andrew was wheeled into church and sat at the front where the pews had been shortened. The congregation were delighted to see him and Tony, our vicar, welcomed him back to St John's after all those months away. It was Andrew's opportunity to be able to thank people for all of their prayers and support. Of course this time we were unable to go up to the altar rail for communion but we were brought communion and had it together at the front of the church. It was a very sacred moment for me because we hadn't been together in church for such a long time.

At 3:10pm on Tuesday 6th June Andrew said his farewells to the staff of 7Y. Dr Chu had come to say goodbye and Andrew was presented with a "Goodbye & Good luck" card and had several goodbye kisses from the female nurses (I wish I had been there!!) Nearly twenty-two weeks after first admission he was leaving this specialist centre and starting out on a new adventure. He would miss his friends a lot and one of the comments in Andrew's card captured the situation extremely well "Andy... the ward won't be the same!" I think he was also a bit apprehensive and nervous about having to leave and settle in to a new environment, but it was to prove an extremely fruitful two months, coming at the right time, just at the beginning of the summer. Dr Chu had told Andrew that he would be under the care of an "excellent team of haematologists." Obviously Andrew was still under the consultants at the Royal and would come back to see them periodically at clinics, to check on his overall progress. According to Dr Chu, Andrew was "a very important patient" and so they would definitely be keeping in close contact with Fazakerley YDU to monitor his progress. It was the beginning of a new chapter and as Mum, Dad and I drove the short journey that evening to visit him in his new home, there was an air of intrepidation about the whole thing.

From the moment we walked through the large double doors of the Younger Disabled Unit, we knew that this was going to be a very good move for Andrew. The day room was open and spacious with a drinks machine, table tennis table, snooker table and a colour television with comfortable chairs and plenty of books to read. Andrew's ward was a small side room with four beds and patio door which led outside to a patio with benches and well kept grounds. It was an extremely pleasant environment and seemed more like a "medical hotel" than a hospital. There was no smell of disinfectant in the air and the atmosphere was relaxed rather than intense and clinical. I believed Andrew would be happy here and I was right. His daily routine consisted of three nutritious high calorie meals, two sessions of

Physiotherapy with an open time limit if at all possible and a period of Occupational Therapy in the afternoon. Once every two weeks there was a social excursion and Andrew was able to come home for the weekend and stay from Friday night till Monday morning. He would have a full blood count every week in order to monitor his disease and when he saw Dr Chu at clinic on 23rd June, Dr Chu remarked, "I am so pleased to see you looking well. You deserve a bit of good news Andrew." Andrew was making excellent progress and it was wonderful to be part of what was happening.

CHAPTER ELEVEN

HAPPIER SUMMERS

WITH ANDREW safely installed in Fazakerley Younger Disabled Unit (YDU) and undergoing an intensive programme of Physiotherapy, Occupational Therapy and sound diet! the long hot months of June and July provided a welcome respite from the traumas of the previous five months. Fazakerley was only twenty minutes from home and as Andrew's mobility was getting better and better, we were able to take him out in the evenings to enjoy the long summer sunsets and explore the surrounding vicinity. Somehow the whole routine of hospital visiting had been broken up and as Andrew wasn't bed-ridden as he had been at the Royal, it didn't really feel like going to hospital, the YDU was a half way house between full hospital care and home.

There is something very special about Andrew's personality. On the exterior there appears to be a quietness and shyness but underneath there is a very warm person who is full of humour and even a sense of mischief, and there is a beautiful smile which illuminates Andrew's face. It was no surprise that he had been so quietly popular at the Royal with nurses, doctors and even two consultants, there was something about him which people felt naturally at ease with. It was no surprise to our family when he immediately took to the staff at Fazakerley and became a very popular patient. There would be numerous occasions in the next two months where I arrived in the evening to find Andy in the staffroom chatting away and having a laugh with the nurses. Eventually the family became redundant on Wednesday evenings because Andrew decided to start playing Badminton (in his wheelchair of course) with some of the nurses in the nearby Gym

Halls! It was such a wonderful sight seeing Andy enjoy the things that we take so easily for granted, and I remember thanking God for the transformation that had occurred from February when a bed ridden, seven stone waif had to be turned round in bed and was so weak he couldn't even lift a mug and had to drink with a straw, to a young man coming bounding down the corridor with his Zimmer frame, his new hair starting to come back, putting on weight and dressed in full, doing weights at Physiotherapy. It was nothing short of a miracle and it could only be seen to be believed. How much God had answered our cries and our prayers we would never really know. The Scripture seemed so profoundly true:-

If my people who are called by my name would humble themselves and pray, and seek my face and turn from their wicked ways, then will I hear from heaven and will forgive their sin and heal their land. (2 Chronicles 7 v14)

In a short book like this there isn't really the time and space to chronicle accurately the events of these two months. All I can do is remember a few of them and perhaps share why they were so important to Andrew and to all of us who shared this precious time together.

One of the side effects of Andrew's first course of chemotherapy was the damaging of the nerve endings in his feet which meant that he was unable to move his feet properly and this obviously would make walking virtually impossible. This 'peripheral neuropathy' was caused by one of the drugs that Andrew had had, called Vincristine, but he was just very unlucky because it didn't effect everybody in the same way. However, when he arrived at Fazakerley, the medical team decided that in order to get Andrew back on his feet again, not only would he need intensive physiotherapy on his legs to get rid of the contractures and build up the muscles again, but they would also need to fit Andrew with some foot splints which would help to keep his feet in their proper position rather than having "foot drop." These splints were duly made and fitted to Andy's feet but they were so cumbersome that it was going to prove very difficult to get his feet into any shoes. So on the evening of the 12th July we set off in my little Metro (with wheelchair in the boot) with a mission to find some shoes which would fit! We ended up at Makro in Kirkby of all places and after much decision making we finally found a pair of trainers that fitted - Size 12! and they were real 'clod hoppers' but they did the trick. We returned to the YDU triumphant and the nurses all wanted to have a look at Andrew's new footwear.

When Andrew was home for weekend leave in the summer I remember him being invited to the Pathfinder Youth Club Barbeque. Of course it takes people a while to get used to the 'culture shock' of seeing someone who they used to remember as able bodied, being confined to a wheelchair. (Fortunately by the time Andrew left Fazakerley he had made so much progress he was walking with sticks). Young people however, have very few inhibitions and Andy was so easily accepted. I remember in the games after the meal we were playing rounders and he was being the bowler from the centre of the playground in his wheelchair with his baseball cap on. These things seem so insignificant but when we thought about what Andrew had come through, it was truly miraculous to see him being able to do so many things again, including playing rounders!

Our birthday was a very special occasion as we celebrated twenty-five years of being twins. When I looked back to the black months of the beginning of the year, I realised how thankful I was to God that Andrew was here to celebrate his birthday. He received so many cards and presents and at the weekend we went out into town with Mum and Dad to have a birthday meal together which was a real treat after months of hospital food! He even donned a shirt and tie to celebrate. My final memory of these wonderful summer months was a service we went to at church on the 9th July. It was a 6:30 service to celebrate the Sixtieth anniversary of Pathfinders, but it was also a service of farewell to our Youth leader, Ken Owen, who was leaving to become a Curate at Heswall, Wirral. Ken had been our English teacher at school and had been a great influence on mine and Andrew's Christian life. So Andrew definitely wanted to get to church. Despite the setback of having shingles we managed to attend and there was a particular part of the service I will always remember. We had of course put Andrew's wheelchair next to the pew and he was sitting for most of the service because he was not walking at this point (without a Zimmer frame). There came a point in the service where we were asked to face the back to thank God for the past, face the middle and pray for each other, face the outside and pray for Christians in other churches and Pathfinder groups. Finally, we were asked to stand and face the front of the church as we prayed for the future. At this point Andrew stood up and clinging onto the pew in front with great determination, he prayed and we committed the future to God. I had my arm around him and although all he had done was stand, it was very emotional. God had brought us through months of turmoil. We didn't know what the future held but we had committed ourselves into God's hands.

Andrew attended clinic at the Royal Liverpool on Friday 28th July the day after his birthday. He was told that his progress was good and he was "most definitely" in remission. It was wonderful news but the euphoria was soon over. Two weeks later we were back in the Royal and the news was not so good. By God's grace Andrew had had two wonderful summer months at Fazakerley and had begun to live again.

CHAPTER TWELVE

RELAPSE

AS WE DROVE back to Fazakerley one evening after taking Andrew for a drive and a drink, he was sitting next to me in the passenger seat. I suddenly noticed out of the corner of my eye that his neck was swollen at the side and he had been complaining about a sore throat. It was Tuesday 1st August and when we got back to the YDU Andrew got hold of a mirror and examined himself. The glands in his neck were swollen and you could feel lumps in certain places. We asked the nurse on duty if they could inform the on call doctor and let Dr Wright, the haematologist at Fazakerley, know what the situation was. Dr Wright was supervising Andrew's care whilst he was undergoing rehabilitation, and he generally came to visit him once a week to discuss his blood count, recommend any changes to his medication and discuss his general progress. He was the spitting image of Jasper Carrot so I always used to smile to myself whenever I saw him!

Dr Wright came over to see Andrew and examine him on the Thursday morning. We were due to go on a YDU day out to Liverpool, to "Ferry across the Mersey!" and the bus was soon about to leave. Dr Wright said it could be an infection which was causing his glands to swell up so he would start him on *Fluconazole and Penicillin and then come to see him on Friday to review the situation. He also said, "It could be Lymphoma." To be honest I think Andrew had already worked out what it was. As we sat on the minibus and waited to set off on our trip to the Mersey Ferry with the other patients, the day had been ruined. Andrew was sitting next to me on the coach and I could see the tears starting to roll down his face. He was very upset and said to me:-

"Oh Mike, I just can't cope if it is."

I put my arm around Andy and tried to comfort him and told him not to worry, to try and enjoy the day. The fact is, I felt so desperately worried I wanted to cry myself. This would have been absolutely no good to Andy so we had a chat and I cheered him up a bit. Twins can almost intuitively know how each other feels sometimes, without need for any words. I knew exactly how he felt because I was feeling exactly the same. You just have to be brave and "keep you pecker up!" as the Professor used to say. We made the best of a hot August day on the River Mersey, sailing up and down and eating a packed lunch which Andrew had balanced on his knees.

It was a good afternoon, and it helped to take Andrew's mind off the situation.

By Friday Dr Wright came over and said that Andrew could go home for the weekend and that his care plan would be maintained. If there was no improvement to his swollen glands by Monday then he would have to contact Ward 7Y and transfer him back to the Royal Liverpool for "further investigations."

It was a tense weekend. There was much examining and prodding of Andrew's neck. There was much debate about whether his swelling was reducing or if the lumps were any softer. We prayed and prayed that it would just be an infection and that antibiotics would do the trick; but deep in my heart I knew we had to face up to the inevitable; it was very depressing but there was no point running away from the hard truth. I felt very angry for the first time in a long while. We had only been told Andrew was "most definitely" in remission on the 28th July and now it looked like, on the 7th August, as if his disease had returned. "That must be the shortest remission on record!" I remember saying to Mum.

Andrew had a sore throat and his swollen glands were still noticeable when he went back to Fazakerley YDU on the Monday. Dr Wright had rung Dr Caswell at the Royal and it had been decided to transfer Andrew back to Ward 7Y. We hadn't been on to 7Y since Andrew had left on Tuesday 6th June. He had made so much progress with his mobility in those two months that he was now able to walk with the aid of walking sticks. The Physiotherapist had done an excellent job on his legs, and his weight was stable at 8 stone 13 lbs (56.5Kg!). He looked so much better than he had done earlier on in the year and had a trendy new hair cut which was starting to grow back!

Tuesday 8th August was a very sad day for us all. Although it was nice to see all the familiar faces of 7Y again we knew what it meant to be back on this ward. As I accompanied Andrew up the corridor Dr Chu was coming down and he stopped to have a chat:

"Andrew, we are totally committed to you. When I heard from Dr Caswell about the swelling in your neck, I said, "Get Mr Andrew back here as soon as possible."

Dr Chu made sure that Andrew had a bed and then he said he would see us on ward round on Thursday, or maybe Wednesday if he had time. As Andrew said, "When someone tells you they are totally committed to you, then you can't say fairer than that!"

Andrew had his 'favourite' operation on the Tuesday. He used to dread the doctors coming to take a sample of *bone marrow because it required a local anaesthetic, but even with this, it was still painful.

The Bone Marrow Aspirate was taken on the Tuesday morning and Dr Creagh, the Senior Registrar came to give him the results not long afterwards. There were abnormal cells in the bone marrow which meant that the disease had returned. In fact the bone marrow report actually said:

"....An early return of the previous acute Leukaemia...."

Andrew's chest X-ray was taken that afternoon and this was fine. A lumbar puncture was taken on the Friday and the cerebro-spinal fluid was also clear. At least this was a bit of a consolation. Dr Chu was due to see Andrew on the Thursday and we already knew that his Lymphoma had relapsed and so I wasn't looking forward to Thursday afternoon at all.

When Dr Chu came round to see Andrew on Thursday 10th August Dad and I were sitting by the bedside.

" Andrew, all I can say is that I'm very, very disappointed. I talk briefly now, then when I finish the ward round I will come back because I want to have a very important conversation with you and your parents."

Andrew was very quiet and I felt sick inside. I disappeared off the ward because I knew I was going to cry and I didn't want to let Andy see me. When Dr Chu returned, he had Ann Brown, the haematology counsellor at his side and they drew the curtains around the bed. Dr Chu began by saying that he wasn't saying that there was nothing he could do for Andrew because there were lots of things he could do. However, he wanted Andrew to be clear:

".....UKALL12, the golden standard has not worked and there is no magic bullet Andrew... there is no new drug that I can give you that has not already been tried...."

All that Dr Chu could do was give Andrew a similar course of chemotherapy to the one he had originally started with in January. This protocol would have to be modified because there was no way Dr Chu could give him two of the drugs he had previously had:-

"I dare not give you L-Asparaginese due to fear of Cerebral stroke. And I can't give you Vincristine because of all the damage it did to your nerves."

His treatment could only consist of the steroid Prednisolone and the Daunorubicin which was a "good drug." After four weeks of this they would take a bone marrow to see if there was any response.

Andrew had already had a history of fungal infections which were "eating him away." If he was to start more chemotherapy he would be again prone to these recurrent infections. To try and counter this problem, Dr Chu was suggesting a low-dose bag of anti-fungal Amphotericin three times a week as a preventative measure to try and reduce the chances of Andrew catching an infection. There were no guarantees. It was all they could do and as Dr Chu left he said to Andrew:-

"......I leave the curtains closed so that you can be alone for a while...."

He took this disappointing news as usual with great calmness and courage but only God knew how he must have felt inside. We were back right where we had begun in January but with ammunition that had been tried before and found wanting.

Andrew started his modified chemotherapy on Friday 11th August. We had written an "Emergency Newsletter" about Andrew which expressed the seriousness of the relapse he had suffered:-

"I cannot stress how important these four weeks are going to be. Andrew needs more prayers now than at any time in the last seven months."

People started to go to church to pray, freshly back from the New Wine festival in Somerset; it was such disappointing news to come back to. Andrew had his back to the wall and we were about to start his treatment all over again. The future was uncertain, only God knew what was in store:-

"I know the plans I have for you," declares the Lord. "Plans to prosper you and not to harm you, to give you a hope and a future." (Jer 29 v11) NIV

CHAPTER THIRTEEN

FUN AND FRIENDSHIP

FOR SOME PEOPLE the prospect of visiting a cancer ward in a large hospital would be something to avoid if they possibly could. They could perceive it as being a place where people come to die. They might think the atmosphere would be depressing and melancholy, as though there was a complete hopelessness about the place. This however, could not be further from the truth. Inevitably visiting a ward like 7Y for a period of months you see the whole range of human emotions. You see people standing in corridors with anxious faces, you see people in tears being comforted by relatives, you see people being wheeled on and off the ward on trolleys and inevitably you see people with beds where the curtains are drawn because they are critically ill or sadly have "passed away." However, there is a positive side which far outweighs the negative one and helps you to feel comfortable and secure. In this microcosm of such a large hospital, literally twenty-five beds, there is much community spirit, camaraderie and laughter! The patients cheer each other up and support each other. The vast majority of the nurses are vivacious and easy to get on with and have a laugh with. In Andrew's case, most of the nursing staff were of a similar age so he found it easy to relate to them. Basically Ward 7Y became to Andrew, and to us, a 'second home' where we felt at ease and where we made lots of new friends in the seven and a half months that he was on the ward.

In those seven and a half months we had many happy times which helped to bring some light relief from the situation that we were all in. In this chapter I want to share a few of them to illustrate the many moments of fun and friendship we had in the last year of Andrew's life. I start with a day when the Professor had to go to a conference and therefore they decided to have the ward round early in the morning, in fact 8:45am to be precise. Andrew was not exactly the model example of an early riser; indeed in hospital sometimes we had to force him to get out of bed! He wasn't that much better at home! On this occasion the doctor came into his side ward that morning and he was instantly protesting:

"Do you know what...... the nurses got me out of bed at 8:30am this morning!"

"The BASTARDS!!" came the instant retort!

Which was not exactly what we were expecting from this clean cut, young doctor with his stripey shirt and trendy ties. There was much laughter!

One of the nurses that Andy got on really well with was also called Andy. This rather large ginger haired young man who was an ex-policeman who liked to play rugby in his spare time, was on the ward when Andrew first came to the Royal on the 4th January. They became instant friends, mainly because they liked to take the mickey out of each other and Andy's sense of humour was similar to 'Ainsdale' humour, which basically meant blatant sarcasm and mickey-taking. The fact that Andy, the nurse, was a Liverpool supporter and we both supported Everton led to instant conflict and opportunities for mickey-taking. When Everton were struggling to beat an Icelandic team in the European Cup this brought great glee to Andy, the nurse, who commented:

".... They can't even manage to play well against the Reykjavik Walrus Herders!!"

The fact that I was a teacher also led to remarks about "These overpaid professions with long holidays who only do five hours work a day!" When Andrew relapsed and was back on Ward 7Y in early August there were a few occasions where he stayed up with Andy and the night staff to play Trivial Pursuit until the early hours of the morning and catch up on the latest hospital gossip! Of course the "first class honours Ph-D chemist" lost on every occasion which gave Andy the nurse great delight! This was also the time when Andy was having difficulty breathing through his nose due to swollen adenoids. On these hot August nights he was apparently snoring his head off and making a rather loud noise which led to a little mischief on behalf of the night staff. When Andrew woke up one morning after another snoring episode there was a letter addressed to "Mr Andrew Ridge" on his bed. I share with you the contents of this mysterious letter:

"Dear Andy,

I do trust you had a good night sleep and are feeling suitably refreshed. I just thought I'd drop you a note concerning one of nature's strangest phenomenon, namely Ridge's nocturnal noises.

Unknown to yourself and probably most of England it was reported in the Los Angeles Tribune that an earthquake measuring 8.2 on the Richter scale occurred overnight. However upon tracing its epicentre they found it to originate from the middle bed on the right, Room 6 Ward 7Y. Upon hearing this news I immediately called the fire brigade and the city civil engineer to assess any damage to the hospital and unfortunately the whole place will be demolished at 7:30am Monday. Never mind. What a pity! Oh dear!

Further more we also had a visit from the noise abatement society who fined me £1,000,000 for being in possession of a noisy patient (I've offered to pay 50p a month).

I did phone your parents and some people at Durham to see if they'd take you off my hands but they declined saying the past six months has been so quiet and peaceful and anyhow who's this Ridge chap I was talking about? I guess you know who your friends are now, hey?

Following this less than fruitful exchange I decided I could possibly make some money out of your unique nightly thunder claps so I called Norris or Ross McWerter (the one who wasn't killed by the IRA) to see if we could get you mentioned in the Guinness Book of Records. This also failed as when he answered his phone I heard him scream "Arrrggghhh! What's that terrible noise?" Oh my ear drums have just burst and he ran away. So much for a few bob to buy some more flowers for my garden.

Finally, at my wits end and wondering what to do and having to stop Roy (next bed) from jumping out of the window, I had a call from Steven Spielberg. Andy lad he said (we're very close you know) I'm in lumber me old mate sunny Jim fella me lad (as I said we're very close).

As it turns out he's just in the middle of making Jurassic Park II and his sound effects chap has just run off with a one legged balding Swedish limbo dancer and he still requires some dinosaur noises to finish the film off.

At this point you provided us with one or your mega decibel nasal noises. "That's it! That's it!" the superstar film director shouted. "That is perfect! What is it?" I then explained the full facts, and hey presto you're signed (Don't forget as manager I get 50%)

Oh yes, I forgot your part. In Jurassic Park one there was a scene where a Brontosaurus sneezed. In this film, there's a scene where a Tyrannosaurus Rex farts and that's where you come in!

All the very best superstar. See you tonight,

Andy (Super staff nurse)"

What is it about students that they have fetishes and appreciate the stupid and ridiculous? When I was a student everybody was obsessed with Neighbours and you had to fight for a place in the television room in the JCR as what seemed to be the whole of Collingwood College piled down from lunch to the compulsive viewing of the day!

With Andrew, he was the ultimate Mr Blobby fanatic! In the Chemistry Department at Durham he walked around with a lab coat with a Mr Blobby on the back. He was affectionately know by some of his colleagues as "Blobby." This however was not enough. Andrew had even pursued this fetish to visiting a Mr Blobby Roadshow at the Gateshead Metrocentre! When the news hit Durham that Andrew was in hospital with cancer this was the beginning of an influx of Mr Blobby paraphernalia including sweets, activity books, audio tapes and inevitably the blow up, inflatable Mr Blobby lookalike which took pride of place above the bed on Ward 7Y. Mr Blobby was not safe however. When Andrew returned from weekend leave late in August he was very concerned because Mr Blobby had mysteriously disappeared. However we soon found out that he had indeed been kidnapped by the 7Y night staff who were demanding a hefty ransom.

The notice above the bed had been carefully put together with newspaper letters so as to conceal the identity of the kidnappers:-

"We have got Mr Blobby. Pay £75,000 or you'll be sorry!"

The excitement was too much for Mr Blobby. When he returned he just couldn't cope with all the secrets of Ward 7Y and Andy's brother. One morning Andy woke up to find a bandaged Mr Blobby hanging from the drip stand next to his bed with a note saying "I just couldn't take it anymore!"

Finally it was the summer when the infamous "Take That!" were doing a concert at the Manchester Arena. It seemed that most of the female staff of Ward 7Y were going to see them but I went with my friend Rachel on the Tuesday and so had the programme to show the gang which included, Clare, Philippa, Lynn and Rose. The male nursing staff it has to be said were suitably unimpressed by this. Andy described me "as a very, very sad person to be going to see Take That!" But the Ridge twins were already converted, buying all 3 CDs when Andy was home one weekend and playing Take That songs on the ward, at low volume of course to avoid ridicule and embarrassment!

In the Bible the Book of Ecclesiastes talks about the rhythm of life very eloquently:-

> *There is a time for everything,*
> *and a season for every activity under heaven:*
> *a time to be born and time to die*
> *a time to weep and a time to laugh....*
> *a time to mourn and a time to dance.*

> (Ecclesiastes 3 v1,2,4) NIV

In a year with so much heartache and tears, it was so wonderful to have times of fun and friendship. They brought light relief to a desperate situation and most importantly of all they buoyed Andrew's spirits and helped him to cope when it would have been easy to get depressed and give up. The long hot summer of 1995 went on and we waited for news of any response to Andrew's treatment.

CHAPTER FOURTEEN

RADIOTHERAPY

IT WAS THURSDAY 31st August 1995 and ward round with Dr Chu. Despite three weeks of treatment using the modified UKALL12 protocol Andrew's *adenoids, tonsils and lymphoma cells in his neck had proved resistant to chemotherapy and he was still finding swallowing and breathing through his mouth difficult. This had been Andrew's third course of chemotherapy and the future was starting to look very uncertain.

Andrew was always a polite and amenable patient. Usually when his consultants came to see him he would always respond to the question, "How are you, Andrew?" in two ways: "I'm fine" or "I'm OK!" Sometimes I wished he would be a bit more forceful and actually tell them how he really felt and if he was frustrated by anything. This was however, not in Andrew's nature. He had always been a very patient and thoughtful person and his temperament had been a great help in the way he had dealt with his illness over the last eight months. I was far more impetuous and impatient and had always been very inquisitive from a very early age. Whether I would have coped as well as Andrew if the tables had been turned is debatable.

However, today the consultant was in for a shock. Dr Chu and the haematology counsellor Ann Brown came to talk to Andrew at the end of the ward round and drew the curtains around his bed so that this could be a private conversation. Today Andrew was not OK or fine. He was "fed up".

"Andrew, I can understand why you are fed up," replied Dr Chu looking very concerned.

They were very disappointed that there had been no clinical improvement in Andrew's disease despite UKALL12. Now it appeared they were genuinely running out of ideas about what to do next. They were being perfectly honest with Andrew:- "Andrew, I don't know what we are going to do." It was obviously a time for desperation but Andrew had an idea which he wanted to offer:-

"What about Radiotherapy?"

There was a pause whilst Dr Chu considered this suggestion and then he replied that he could try to arrange an emergency appointment with Dr Myint, the consultant radiologist from Clatterbridge Centre of Oncology who would be in clinic tomorrow in the Royal. Ann Brown would accompany Andrew to the appointment and hopefully he might get into Clatterbridge for next week. Now, it was the patient who was making the suggestions as regards treatment, but when the alternative is to call it a day and sit back and wait to die, which 25-year old wouldn't want to make suggestions? What had impressed me about this conversation was not just Andrew's imagination but the fact that his consultant was not deserting Andrew and telling him, "I'm sorry, there's absolutely nothing more we can do for you." They were still trying to open doors and explore avenues for treatment which did not instil a sense of false hope but at least gave Andrew a glimmer of hope, which is better than no hope at all. This reflected the absolute commitment of the medical team to Andrew which had been constant right from the moment he had arrived at 7Y on 4th January, over eight months ago. We were so grateful that we could put absolute trust in these people without being suspicious or wondering whether there was a hidden agenda that was being kept from us. Andrew had his appointment with Dr Myint at clinic on the Friday morning. As the consultant had said, "You're stuck between the Devil and the deep blue sea." It was obviously worth a try but there could be no guarantees about the success of the treatment. Andrew was already on a Steroid called Prednisolone, and it was decided that he should be kept on this because often it helped the Radiotherapy to shrink the tumour cells by producing a certain reaction. So Andrew was booked into Clatterbridge for Monday 4th September 1995 for a two week course of Radiotherapy.

Andrew was transferred by ambulance to Clatterbridge Centre of Oncology on Monday and Mum followed in the car with all of his belongings. His visit proved to be a very short one. He had just settled into his private room on Conway Ward when the doctor came to tell him that his blood counts were too low for him to have a two week progressive course of Radiotherapy. Instead he was to have one dose of Radiation today and then go back to the Royal where his progress would be reviewed at Friday clinic. So Andrew's neck was marked with pens to pinpoint his treatment. He had five minutes of High dose Cobalt 60 gamma radiation, two and a half minutes on each side of his neck. He didn't feel a thing. By the time I arrived at the Royal he was back in Ward 7Y to the surprise of the nurses who thought he was going for two weeks. We would now have to wait and see if there would be any response. We had prayed hard that weekend that Andrew's Radiotherapy would be effective and the weekly newsletter had focused on his forthcoming treatment at Clatterbridge.

"Pray that Andrew's emergency radiotherapy will be effective in destroying malignant Lymphoma cells in Andrew's neck and tonsils."

Indeed after we had seen Dr Chu we had been down to the chapel to pray that God would open doors and allow Andrew to have further treatment. Our prayers had been answered but we still had to wait and see if the Radiotherapy would be effective.

As the week progressed we could see with our own eyes the improvement. The lumps in Andrew's neck felt softer and the swelling was coming down. His grossly enlarged tonsils were beginning to reduce in size and his swallowing was getting easier despite having a sore throat. You could see it with your eyes and you didn't need to be a doctor to realise the treatment was working! Again God had answered our prayers in a most remarkable way. Andrew went to see Doctor Myint at clinic on Friday where he recommended a similar dose on Monday 11th September. By this time the reduction in his tonsils was over

50% and his comments in Andrew's medical notes spoke for themselves:

"……..a remarkable response to Radiotherapy…"

One of the problems with Andrew's swollen tonsils and adenoids was that it would be virtually impossible to anaesthetise him in order to put a Hickman line in, which would be necessary for further courses of Chemotherapy. However, now that Andrew's tonsils and adenoids were reducing in size, what had seemed an impossible operation was starting to look feasible again.

Andrew went back to Clatterbridge for a second dose of Cobalt 60 gamma radiation on Monday 11th September. He had an infection on the Tuesday which was quickly dealt with by *Piperacillin and *Gentamicin antibiotics. By Thursday when Professor Cawley came round, his swollen neck was much improved and his tonsils were nearly back to normal size. Andrew would be able to go home for weekend leave and next week he would have the operation to have a Hickman Catheter put in. The Professor explained that Andrew would be having a new course of Chemotherapy called Mini-Beam which is used in the treatment of High Grade Lymphomas. This would be a cocktail of drugs called BCNU, Etoposide, Ara-C and Melphalan over a six day period. It would be Andrew's fourth course of Chemotherapy and was obviously a last resort treatment, but the Radiotherapy Andrew had suggested had been a vital stepping stone which he had needed in order to have more aggressive treatment. The Radiotherapy, in the short term, had been a great success and it was time to fight on.

CHAPTER FIFTEEN

FIGHTING ON

O N WEDNESDAY 20th September we went down to the hospital chapel to pray. It was the evening before Andrew's new treatment was about to begin. The Mini-Beam was a last ditched attempt to try and get back on top of his disease. As he sat in his wheelchair and I held my arm around him he prayed with real courage, fighting back the tears that were welling up:

"Dear Lord.... I know I have a terrible disease.... Please help me to trust you. Help this treatment to be successful."

In Jesus name. Amen."

This was indeed a terrible disease and if I had known that we were in the last month of Andrew's life I think I would have stayed in the Chapel another hour that night. It was a place of security where earlier on in the year I had pleaded with God for Andrew's life and he had been given a second chance.

Andrew had his first dose of BNCU on the Thursday morning and on the Friday he had a splitting headache, slept all day and was generally feeling ill. When I visited him that evening and saw his fragile body hiding under the sheets it reminded me of the bed-ridden young man who had spent most of the beginning of the year in hospital. We just couldn't go through it all again, could we? Andrew got through the six day course of treatment but on the Tuesday 26th September he was feeling dizzy and his blood pressure was lower then usual. Looking rather jaundiced and with a liver function that was definitely not normal the doctors had been getting rather concerned.

He was also showing a fluctuating temperature and it was looking increasingly likely that his recurrent fungal infection on his chest had come back, especially as his doses of amphotericin were being gradually increased from 30mg to 60mg and then to 90mg IV. The Professor had said to him on ward round that he was on a "strong regime" of antibiotics which should cover all angles. His bone marrow was flat and with low blood counts because of his active chemotherapy it would take a couple of weeks for his counts to recover before they could assess his response to the treatment.

It was about this time that we had our dealing with the hospital Social Worker which proved to be a very salutary experience. One of Andrew's greatest loves was his car and being able to drive. As a little boy he had always talked about saving for a new car as being the first thing he would aim to do when he got older. On student finances he could only afford to run an old Metro which we had bought together for the grand sum of £850 in September 1992. His illness had led to his inability to drive as one of the drugs that he had had during his treatment was *neurotoxic and had damaged the nerve endings in his feet. He was therefore unable to move his feet sufficiently to operate a clutch or accelerator and it caused a great deal of unhappiness and frustration for Andrew that he was no longer able to get behind the wheel of a car. He was also dependent on me for all his travelling and he used to joke that it was less dangerous being in hospital with Lymphoblastic Lymphoma than being a passenger in a car when I was driving!! We wanted to try and remedy Andrew's frustration and provide him with some short-term goals which would be something to aim for and hopefully help to keep him happy and motivated. In retrospect we had perhaps left it a bit too late in the day. One of Andrew's fellow patients in Room 6 had told him about 'Motability' which is basically a disability benefit which he could apply for and then the money could be signed over to a car leasing scheme which lasted for two or three years. The car would be specially modified so that Andrew who was officially 'disabled' under his entitlement would be able to get to drive. Andrew was obviously very interested in this scheme, particularly if it meant he could drive a Vauxhall Corsa Breeze which was one of his favourite cars. We were dispatched to the nearby Vauxhall Garages in Liverpool to get hold of the car brochures and price lists and it was providing a very healthy stimulus for Andrew who had something to aim for. The forms which he needed were duly filled and they went via the hospital Social Worker who sent them to the appropriate place. She came to visit him again on the 3rd October 1995 to tell him Yes, he was entitled to the benefit but he wouldn't be able to get a car because the leasing scheme was for two or three years and he had "a terminal illness and was only expected to live another six months." Initially shocked by what she had said, and after brooding for a while, Andrew in typical style, got himself out of bed and went off in his wheelchair and phoned the headquarters of Motability in Blackpool. Convinced that the social worker had made 'a cock up' he was told that he would be able to get a car after all. By now though, the damage had been done. We were extremely upset and disappointed by the apparent insensitivity of this social worker who had told him he only had another six months to live. We had never at any stage been told by any of Andrew's consultants that Andrew had a terminal illness and had six months to live. How could somebody who wasn't even a clinician be telling Andrew such sensitive information as though it was common knowledge? Of course we knew that Andrew was seriously ill and time was running out. I had already talked to the Professor and asked him "if Mini-Beam doesn't work are we at the end of the line?" to which he had replied "Yes, I think we probably are." So I was well aware that we were in the closing stages of Andrew's illness but we wanted to remain positive and we were not just going to give up and give in to this disease. I believe she could have been more diplomatic in what she had said. The Professor offered to make Mum an appointment with the social worker the next day but we decided to decline because really the words had already been said and the damage had already been done. It was the first time in our experience of Andrew being in hospital that we felt annoyed and upset that something could have been handled so insensitively. Although it wasn't the medical teams fault; it was the social worker we were annoyed at. We were not trying to pretend that Andrew was going to carry on indefinitely as though we somehow didn't want to face up to the truth. It was fundamental to be positive to keep hoping and praying because we were both Christians and it didn't seem right just to give up and let Andrew sit back and die. He had survived an incredibly stormy course of treatment at the beginning of the year so there was always hope. We felt the same as Jamie Bowen who had been in the national press that year as Child B, the little girl who was refused a second transplant on the NHS and was having new experimental treatment (Donor Lymphocyte Infusion) for her acute Myeloid Leukaemia:

"I say: 'Never give up unless you are just on the last little drop of life you have in you'."

If I was totally honest, I would say that after this little episode Andrew lost some of his tenacious desire to stay alive. In the two weeks following this incident he became weaker and weaker and was complaining of a sore throat which was causing him a lot of pain. I took time off work from the 5th October because I had become very concerned as I saw Andrew becoming gradually weaker and his condition deteriorate.

His neck was still swollen and on 10th October he was put on Diamorphine in order to ease the pain that he had from a sore throat which he had described to one of the nurses as "a stabbing pain…. with a pain score of 7 out of 10."

Alarm bells immediately started to ring in my head. Did this Diamorphine pump mean palliative care before death? However, the doctors were still carrying on with all of his treatment. He had started the GCSF treatment to boost his infection fighting neutrophils and with the consultants permission his amphotericin was changed to the less toxic ABLC to treat his fungal infection. We had been in this situation twice already. We knew very well that infections could be life threatening and that with a flat marrow and no neutrophils it could easily get the better of him, even with intravenous antibiotics.

Until his counts went up it was difficult to assess his response to the chemotherapy so we carried on and then all of a sudden, totally unexpected, the event we had been warned of so often over the last nine months happened. Andrew had fought to the bitter end, it was now time to let go.

CHAPTER SIXTEEN

THE DEATH OF A TWIN BROTHER

WE HAD BEEN at the hospital since 1:30pm on Sunday. Although the news had been bad, all the fear had gone and an awesome expectation had replaced it. For those who had come from afar there were the tears which accompanied the shock of seeing the Andy they loved lying down and using oxygen to aid breathing. We had survived nine and a half months of bad news. Somehow the past had helped us to prepare for the moment we had been warned of so often but which had never arrived. We had helped a frail young man (with coat, baseball cap, trainers and 2 walking sticks) to the car on the Saturday evening and we could see the weariness and tiredness beginning to grow, that, as before, everything was becoming an effort. How wonderful that Andy had been home to the security of the place he loved. To sit on the sofa, to go upstairs on his bottom, to lie on his bed, to listen to the CDs he loved, to talk to his brother and friend. To try and watch Blind Date in between dozing and then to leave his home and go back to the hospital where he would die three days later. When he had argued with the registrar and nurse on Saturday morning about going home to stay overnight it was as though through the banter he knew it would be his last chance to be at home and secure with the people he loved.

I had sat with him through Sunday and Monday night. Helped him with his oxygen mask, helped him when he needed the toilet, spoken to him and he knew I was always there. I remember the Professor, looking rather embarrassed, sitting on his bed on the Monday afternoon and asking Andy how he was and he pulled off his mask and said, "Not as good as I was, but

I'm OK!" I remember the conversation in the doctor's office "Words are just inadequate, the worst type of this disease I've ever seen. Terrible, terrible." I didn't want to spend more time talking to doctors, somehow it was more important to be at the bedside with Andrew.

On the Tuesday morning he had had a bed wash and acknowledged the nurses whilst I was catching up on some sleep. From the Tuesday afternoon onwards, he was sleeping, only occasionally stirring to open his eyes, but so wonderfully comfortable. Every part of his body was cushioned, the bed was a sea of white, white sheets, white towel behind his head, fluffy white seal at his side, Brilliant White! His breathing had changed on the Tuesday around 4pm when Andy and Fran had turned him over. From 5:30pm till 9pm nobody left the bedside because they said it was very close. The chaplain came and prayed and we spoke to him. I remember Dad saying, "I love you Andy, always have, and always will." My mum, crying said, "You have no idea how much I have loved you, you children have been my life." We read from Romans 8 and said Psalm 23 together and we sang the songs that had meant so much to us both in the past. Suddenly they took on a whole new meaning

You are beautiful beyond description.
Be still for the presence of the Lord.
Jesus, name above all names.
Shine Jesus Shine.
Come on and celebrate.
Jesus we enthrone you.
There is a redeemer.
Hallelujah,My Father.
Majesty.
Isn't He wonderful?
The grace of God

They seemed to flood back into my memory. Even the songs from Les Miserables that we had seen together, "Bring him home" and "Do you hear the people sing?" There was no concept of time. It must have been around three and a half hours but it felt timeless.

The day shift said goodbye and Chris the staff nurse who was on during the night came on. We discussed the antibiotics and decided they should go up as Andy would have wanted to die fighting his infection. Andy was still with us. He hadn't died when they had predicted. His breathing was easier although shallow but his *Cheyne Stoke respiration had stopped. The night carried on. We were all starting to get tired ourselves. I remember kissing Andy on his cheeks, I remember touching his new hair that had started to grow, dampening his mouth and touching his lovely bushy eyebrows. The doctor who Andy had been so fond of, Martin, came and sat on the bed and said hello, spoke to us all and then smiled and left us. He had been such a wonderful support through these hellish months. It was wonderful he had just happened to be on call that evening.

The ward was asleep and night-time was slipping into daytime. The oxygen still hissed and he carried on sleeping. At 6:45am he twitched and I said "Mum." Everyone stirred and we watched the shallow breathing was starting to ebb, the breathing was getting gentler and more sudden, the breathing slowed and slowed and slowed and then Andrew's eyes opened and we saw one last glimpse of those wonderful hazel eyes, the eyelids were so prominent, and he must have been staring into Mum's eyes because she was sitting on the side where he was facing, I was holding his hand. He just stopped breathing and the oxygen was turned off and everything went quiet and there was absolute stillness. He was still warm and the tension of the grip of his hand in mine had gone, and I laid my hand delicately on the top of his head and prayed and then my Mum started to say the Lord's prayer and all six of us prayed and dear Andrew had gone. How beautiful because he had eased out of one world and into another. No fear, no restlessness, no pain just sleeping and then sleeping no more. We were stunned but it was so awesome. We had glimpsed something that was beyond this world which I will never forget. It was a glimpse of eternity, of a life that had changed. The beginning of a new world for the son of God who had left this one. We stood in silence and looked upon the twin whose life had been so rich. We said our goodbyes and then walked to the quiet room whilst they made him comfortable. We came back. His eyes were closed and he had a black eye on his left side. His arms were laid out straight. Complete with pink carnation on his chest and fluffy white seal (Sealy) at his side he was at peace and at rest. The awful ordeal of nine and a half months was over. The uncertainty had gone and there was release, relief and freedom.

We said our final goodbyes and I took a last glimpse of Andy before I left the ward at about 8:20 am. The nurses were gathered at the nurses' station and we had a tearful goodbye. All those who had been there at the beginning were here at the end, to share the pain. Staff nurse Andy, John, Cilla, Julie, Cynthia, Lisa, Pippa, Sara. He had come into Ward 6 of 7Y on Wednesday 4th January 1995 and he had died in Ward 6 of 7Y on Wednesday 18th October 1995, forty-one weeks later after first admission. As I came to the end of the corridor, staff nurse John Murray came up and hugged me. Fighting back the tears he said, "Please don't forget us, keep in touch, come and see us." I never expected to see the nurses cry, but they had become friends and I will never forget the good times we spent on the ward.

We took the lift, and pushing Andrew's wheelchair full of his belongings, we walked the long corridor to the main exit. Into the fresh air of a Wednesday morning in mid October. Grey clouds and a morning chill. I put my arm around my Mum as we walked up the service road to the stairs. We drove away in my auntie's car and I took one last look at the pink curtains of the window on the 7th floor. We drove out of Liverpool between 8:30 and 9:00am on the Wednesday morning. The city was wakening and the traffic was coming into work on a normal Wednesday morning. I saw a double decker bus full of people, I saw school girls in uniform, talking, walking, hurrying to school, the world was turning round, life was going on and amid the hustle of a new day in Liverpool my brother's world had just come to an end. It was an unreal feeling, a time warp. We had just watched the most important event in my life unfold in front of my eyes and the world seemed to say, "It's a normal day." I will miss my brother deeply. He has been a part of our lives for twenty-five years and I spent immeasurable hours with him this year. No-one can replace him and no-one can take away the pain of not being able to see him, talk to him and be with him any more. But his death was unimaginably beautiful and will help to console me in the years to come. I know that he is safe in God's hands, and one day I will see him again.

CHAPTER SEVENTEEN

HOPE FROM THE FUNERAL

IT IS VERY DIFFICULT to describe how we felt in the six days between Andrew's death and his funeral. After an ordeal that had lasted for nearly 10 months you would have expected to have felt physically exhausted. However, it is amazing how you can respond in a moment of loss because we found ourselves making plans, organising all the arrangements for the funeral, collecting the death certificate from the hospital, informing the DSS, closing bank accounts and planning the hymns and structure of the funeral service with Tony, our Vicar. Life was almost unreal for those six days. It felt like we were in a time warp. I didn't seem to be bereft and grieving as I imagined I might be. Everything seemed to be "numb" as though we were going around in our own little world and the outside world seemed detached from our experiences. Andrew's death had not been how I imagined it to be and my response was also not as I had imagined it would be. We certainly grieved and felt the tremendous loss in the months that followed, but this interim period was very strange.

I went down to church to pray on the Wednesday evening at 9:00pm, just as we had done in the previous months. I was expecting to drive into the church car park and be met by my close friend Steve, who had been such a pillar of strength and had co-ordinated all the prayer meetings as well as ringing the Royal each night to get the news on Andrew's progress. As I drove into the car park, there was a group of around 20-30 people milling around. Most of all I remember vividly noticing the twins, Helen & Louise, who are in the Pathfinder group, standing together. It suddenly struck me. I am no longer a twin, my brother is no longer at my side. There was much hugging and tears as I tried to console people who were upset and grieving for Andy. The support we had received from this group of people had been immense and undiminished over the last ten months. Some of the younger Pathfinders were finding it very hard to see why God had let Andy die after so long and after so much prayer. The leaders were doing their best to answer these most difficult questions but there was no doubt in my mind as to whether God had let us down or not, he simply hadn't. We eventually went into church where I said a few words to tell everyone how it had been when Andy died and to thank them for their months of support and prayer. We then prayed and thanked God for Andrew's life and for his faithfulness up until the end. Lesley Phipps prayed that people's faith would be strengthened not diminished by what had happened, and I am sure that was the case for many people at St John's. Andrew's illness had provided a focus for prayer that had done the church, and many individuals, an immense amount of good. That could never be taken away from us. Of course there would be questions which all of us would ask in the months following his death but God seemed so close that now was not the appointed time to reflect on these things.

As the news of Andrew's death reached the people of Ainsdale and the Chemistry Department at Durham, the phone calls started to flood in and there was a constant stream of cards and letters coming to the door.

One letter especially touched me. It was from the lady who had been so brave enough to come up and pray for Andy on the day he had come to church in January, so early on in his illness. To me it summed up the situation so accurately and eloquently and I have read it several times over the months following Andrew's death. It had been a great source of comfort because it was such a truthful response to what had happened:-

"It was with such sadness that we heard from Steve this morning that Andy had died - our hearts just bled for you - it seemed so cruel after all the ups and downs of the past months. Latterly I have felt so angry with God that Andy's suffering had gone on for so long, to say nothing of that of you and your parents watching him - especially if he was not going to be finally healed. However, in my grief for you this morning, God just quoted Isaiah 55 v8-9 to me:-

For my thoughts are not your thoughts, neither are your ways my ways.

As the heavens are higher than the earth, so are my ways higher than your ways and my thoughts than your thoughts.

There is so little we know or understand. We do quite simply have to trust God, but it can be hard when things appear to be going wrong. Andy of course has been finally "healed" now, but for some unknown reason, not to continue with his life on earth.

You and your parents are going to be very tired for a long time for life has been utterly draining for months. You can however take comfort in the fact that there was nothing more that you, the medical profession or prayer could have done.

May God bless you all and may you feel the comfort of his presence close at hand.

We all loved Andy - though not of course nearly as much as you - he was a very special person and will be missed such a lot.

With our love and prayers

Donald & Angela"

Altogether we received 186 cards and 40 letters of sympathy from all over. Some people have a way with words but there were some messages which were often very simple but touching:-

"I will remember him always"

and

"Andrew will live on in my memory"

were two such examples.

One came from a fellow patient on Ward 7Y:-

"We just wanted to write and tell you how privileged we feel to have met and known Andrew and how lucky he was to have a family who love him as much as you. We will always remember him as will everyone who knew him.

Thinking of you all...."

One message echoed what we had written in the local paper:-

"I have not seen illness borne with such wonderful cheerfulness and faith. Andrew was an inspiration to all who met him. Yours is the great loss."

But perhaps the most poignant of all was from Andrew's former Maths teacher at sixth form, who had visited him in hospital back in February:-

"It gave me great pleasure to see my perfect pupil grow up into a charming young man. How much greater must have been the pleasure that you all had during Andrew's life. And how terrible now your loss......"

These expressions of sympathy gave us great strength and consolation in those strange six days before the funeral, as we realised that we were not alone in our grief and that many people were mourning Andrew's death.

I was determined that Andrew's funeral should be a positive celebration of his life. I wanted it to reflect the way Andrew had dealt with his illness. He had been positive and courageous right up until the day that he died and I believed his funeral should be the same. I also decided that I was going to speak at his funeral. As Andrew's twin brother I felt I was in the best position to talk about Andrew's character and personality, and the way he had been during his illness. This was a difficult decision. Several people warned me that I could be totally overwhelmed by grief and emotion on the day and would not be able to go through with it. On the Monday afternoon I didn't feel able to go through with it! I felt so upset and tormented. However this was to be the last thing I would do for Andrew. I knew that God would be with me and would give me all the strength I needed. He would carry me through as he had done throughout all the difficult moments of the last year.

We went to church on Monday night to pray for the service on Tuesday and to set up the P.A. system as we were playing three songs on tape during the service as a period of quiet reflection. The musicians were also having a practice. Andy used to play the guitar for Pathfinders and CYFA when he was home from University and we had picked two choruses which he had loved and which had very uplifting words. Myself, Mum and Natalie had been to see Andrew at the chapel of rest that afternoon. Tomorrow was to be his special day.

The church was packed as we followed Andrew's coffin into St John's at 2:30pm on Tuesday 24th October 1995. Some people came in later, after Andrew's family had been shown to their seats, and there was standing room only.

I was sitting next to my sister, Natalie, who had told me not to look at her during the first hymn because she is very emotional and it was my turn to give my Eulogy at the end of this first hymn! I knew if I saw her crying I would probably begin to cry myself and then be no good to anybody when it was my turn to speak! We remained standing to sing the first hymn "Abide With Me." The words are incredibly moving especially the fourth verse which speaks about the triumph over death for those who belong to Christ:-

> *I fear no foe with thee at hand to bless;*
> *Ills have no weight and tears no bitterness.*
> *Where is death's sting? Where grave, thy victory?*
> *I triumph still if though abide with me.*

It was time to speak about Andrew. As I walked up to the lectern I had butterflies in my stomach but I felt composed and I placed my red Bible on the shelf and a photo of Andy and my notes on the top of the lectern. There was what seemed to be a sea of faces in front of me as I began:-

"As the Professor of Haematology said last Monday, 'Words are just inadequate.' Whatever I say today is such a poor reflection on how it feels to lose a twin, and especially somebody as wonderful as Andrew. It's like losing your right arm - he is, and always will be, irreplaceable.

Andy was brilliant academically, clever enough to go to Oxford but wise enough to realise that in life, happiness is far more important than status - so he moved to Durham and was successful in his chemistry degree with 1st class honours, and he continued to work as a postgraduate up until December 1994, researching into Organic Chemistry.

I remember walking home from school with him after the Maths exam in 1986, having a post mortem of the exam, arguing over who had solved the problem in the correct way - I got a C and he got an A so the answer was pretty obvious!!

He was an extremely UNTIDY person! Wherever he went he created a mess. We used to nearly come to blows about the state of the bedroom at home. His idea of making a bed were sheets in a big lump in the middle, duvet thrown over the top, a bit like Mount Everest sticking out from a desert plain!

He had some very strange habits! The only person I have ever met who taped jingles off the radio and played them repeatedly until it nearly drove you bonkers! He had a fetish for Mr Blobby, and became a devoted Mr Blobby fan with an inflatable Mr Blobby above his bed on Ward 7Y, until he was kidnapped by the night staff and £75,000 was demanded in ransom money! He even became a Take That fan in the summer of this year!

He had a rational and analytical mind. He loved to have information at his fingertips, even during his illness. You see it wasn't good enough for Andy for it to be a "yellow antibiotic" on the drip, it had to be ABLC, a lipid complex of Amphotericin used to treat fungal infections. It wasn't good enough to have a low blood count, it had to be Haemoglobin 10.2, Platelets 7 and Neutrophils 0.1. He loved to programme his own drip and to pour his eyes over his prescription chart. He commanded all the information and although he had no control over the final outcome of his illness, he was in total control of his treatment and knew exactly all about it, which helped him to fight even harder.

He was a quietly popular young man, who was warm and humorous with those who he knew well. Never an extrovert, but never as shy as some people imagined. He would have been so touched to see so many of his friends here today.

I shall remember him trekking across America with me. I will remember him dancing to "Saturday Night" by Whigfield in the night-clubs of Mallorca. I will remember him behind the wheel of his Metro, a real shed of a car, "the Wombat" as it became affectionately known, whizzing around Durham. I will remember one hot and humid August evening on the bench outside 7Y Ward chatting to each other and I said to Andy, 'I don't know how you have coped over the last eight months with all this suffering.' He looked at me, as though I was talking an alien language 'What suffering?' he replied. 'I've not really been in any pain! It could have been a lot worse.'

Andrew was an inspiration to all who met him and to me especially. He fought his disease tooth and nail, every complication, and there were so many, he faced it, he got on with it, he never felt sorry for himself or got angry. We used to joke and use the words of Mrs Thatcher before she resigned, "I Fight on. I Fight to Win!"

Finally I will remember his quiet faith in God. He was no Bible basher. He went through some difficult times but being ill suddenly crystallised his need to depend on God. It wasn't a question of God, where are you? It was a question of "Help me Lord in these difficult days"

He died in the knowledge that he is beginning a new life in eternity with Christ. That's why, in an ironic kind of way his death was so beautiful for all those whose privilege it was to be there. He has been healed in dying but EVERY prayer that was said for him sustained him in over nine and a half months of struggle.

His death will never be in vain. He has enriched our lives immensely and given us twenty-five years of wonderful memories. He has caused many people in this church to pray, the effects of which are incalculable. He has demonstrated to us that in life, loving and caring are so, so important. "What makes the desert beautiful?" says a quotation I read in a book recently

"Is that somewhere, far below its surface, it holds a spring of fresh water."

My prayer today for Myself, Mum, Dad and Natalie is that the faith, courage, cheerfulness and hope Andrew showed in his life and during his illness, when he was with us, may be the same faith, courage, cheerfulness and hope which is given to us as we rebuild our lives, and face the future without him.
Amen."

I then read the famous passage from Romans chapter 8 v 29-39. This passage was read to Andrew when he had been critically ill way back in February and on the evening before he died. For me it has become one of the most powerful passages of scripture in the Bible and extremely precious to me personally:-

And we know that all that happens to us is working for our good if we love God and are fitting into his plans. For from the very beginning God decided that those who came to him - and all along he knew who would - should become like His son, so that his son would be the first born, with many brothers. And having chosen us he called us 'not guilty,' filled us with Christ's goodness, gave us a right standing with himself, and promised us his glory.

What can we ever say to such wonderful things as these? If God is on our side, who can ever be against us? Since he did not spare even his own son for us but gave him up for us all, won't he also surely give us everything else?

Who dares accuse us whom God has chosen for his own? Will God?

No! He is the one who had forgiven us and given us a right standing with himself.

Who will then condemn us? Will Christ? No! For he is the one who died for us and came back to life again for us and is sitting at the place of highest honour next to God, pleading for us in heaven.

Who then can ever keep Christ's love from us? When we have trouble or calamity, when we are hunted down or destroyed, is it because he doesn't love us any more? And if we are hungry, or penniless, or in danger, or threatened with death, has God deserted us?

No, for the scriptures tell us that for his sake we must be ready to face death at every moment of the day - we are like sheep awaiting slaughter.

But despite all this, overwhelming victory is ours through Christ who loved us enough to die for us. For I am convinced that nothing can ever separate us from His love.

Death can't, and life can't. The angels won't, and all the powers of hell itself cannot keep Gods love away. Our fears for today, our worries about tomorrow, or where we are - high above the sky or in the deepest ocean - nothing will ever be able to separate us from the love of God demonstrated by our Lord Jesus Christ when he died for us.

(Romans 8 v 29-39 Living Bible Edition)

The great promise that not even death can separate us from God's love is so true and Andrew had loved this passage and truly knew the promises it held out. Our vicar preached on rejoicing for those who life's work was complete and who had stepped into Christ's heavenly kingdom. It was a very positive message and this was followed by some very sensitive and personal prayers by two people who had known Andrew since he was eleven - our former youth leader Rev. Ken Owen and Michelle his wife.

Finally, we played ten minutes of unbroken music so that people could have time for themselves and for reflection. The beautiful "Love moves in mysterious ways" by Julia Fordham was one of Andrew's favourite songs - bought for him for Valentine's Day 1992 by his former girlfriend Dawn. This was followed by two songs from Andrew's favourite musical Les Miserables: "Bring Him Home" and "Do You Hear The People Sing." In many ways this was the most moving and poignant part of the service because it gave people time, not to be talked to, but to sit and think quietly about Andrew.

As we left the church to "Praise My Soul The King Of Heaven" and processed out behind Andrew's coffin the sea of faces suddenly became people who were recognised. Andrew's colleagues from Durham University had come in force. Andy, Clare and Lisa, three of Andy's nurses from Ward 7Y were also there and Jan & Robbie, his nurses at the YDU in Fazakerley were amongst the crowd. Professor Gerald Blake, who had been mine and Andrew's Principal at Collingwood College, Durham where we had both been students had made the long journey. Andrew was so popular and this was reflected by the large number of people who gathered by the graveside at Liverpool Road Cemetery. As Tony led the few sentences of scripture that accompany the lowering of the coffin the sky almost changed colour - it was a wonderful atmospheric and moody sky - I felt as though God was trying to speak to us as Andrew was finally laid to rest. Months of suffering were over but now we were left with the immense task of starting to rebuild our lives. As Andrew's body was laid to rest the sentences of scripture had rung out:-

"I am the Resurrection and the life,
He who believes in me will live even though he dies."
(John 11 v 25)

It was the end of a nine and a half month ordeal. Andrew comes from the Greek word which means 'manly.' One wreath of flowers that lay at his grave said...."to the inspirational bravery of the man you became." In those nine and a half months Andrew has taught us all the meaning of courage. He had been an inspiration to many and he had truly become a man, in the real sense of the word. His funeral was completed and it had been as beautiful as we could have wished for.

CHAPTER EIGHTEEN

A WORD ON SUFFERING

ON ONE LEVEL Andrew's death seems like a terrible tragedy. Here was a young man who had so much potential and so much to offer the world. He was very gifted academically and was trying to make a compound synthetically in a laboratory which occurs in nature in minute quantities, called Vinigrol. It is known to have useful pharmaceutical qualities and anti-hypertensive properties as well as being used to arrest progression from Aids Related Complex (ARC) to Aids. A full synthesis of this compound would have been highly desirable and potentially beneficial in the field of medicine. If his Ph.D had been completed and his research had been successful, who knows what the future might have held? But this talent has been brutally cut short and there will be many who will feel it is a terrible waste.

For my parents it is a terrible waste. The nightmare scenario of losing a child, losing a twin son, will take years to come to terms with, if ever. There seems to be something so horribly wrong with losing a child because usually you die before your children. This is not the natural course of events and makes it even more difficult to come to terms with. The months of bereavement have been desperately dark and very hard. Where once there was a vibrant young man there is now a massive void. Out of the blue, waves of grief put you back months when you felt you may have made a little progress. This is the great difficulty with grief, it is so unpredictable. When a child dies, for you as a mother or father it is as though part of you has died. There is no amount of medication, words or bereavement counselling that can change the feeling of loss. You must learn to live with it. Only the healing power of Christ can make a difference.

For some people it seems incredibly unfair. How could a loving God allow this to happen? How could God have been so cruel to allow Andrew to struggle and suffer for so long, only to die at the end of it? Where's the fairness in that?

This however is a simplistic analysis. It ignores the outstretched arms of Jesus, as he died in agony to redeem a world that had turned its back on God. It also forgets the way in which Andrew dealt with his illness, his supreme courage and faith; whilst outwardly wasting away, inwardly he was being renewed.

You see, for the Christian, death is not the end. The resurrection of Jesus Christ from the dead gives us confidence that when we die we too will be raised to new life, a life which is everlasting and to be enjoyed in God's presence. Andrew truly believed in these promises. C.S. Lewis wrote: "God whispers to us in our pleasures and speaks in our conscience, but shouts in our pain: it is his megaphone to rouse a deaf world" (The Problem of Pain 1940 p74). In 1995 a year of crisis when there seemed to be nothing to depend on, God was more real than ever. Through the pain and suffering Andrew endured, many people came closer to God and could hear his voice more clearly than ever. So many of our prayers were answered and for those who watched Andrew's illness progress there was given a strength and determination to keep on praying and run the race with Andrew until the end.

I am not trying to describe his illness through rose-tinted spectacles and make Andrew sound like a saint. On the contrary, like all of us there were times when he got depressed, got fed up of visitors and was frightened, but at twenty-five years old, when you think you are immortal, to suddenly have to come to terms with a serious illness and the real possibility you are going to die, who wouldn't have got frightened or fed up occasionally! It is true to say that these were rare occasions. On the whole Andrew remained cheerful, optimistic and extremely patient in spite of everything that he had to endure. His attitude to his illness was exemplary. There was never a hint of self pity and Andrew used to say, "I wouldn't wish this on anybody." A God of love gave him this special ability to cope with such a terrible illness.

We talk about miracles. Today miracles do happen occasionally but when we read the gospels we see Jesus miraculously healing those who came to him. Today, even doctors would admit that very occasionally, very rarely, people unexpectedly get better, even from serious illness like cancer, and it is almost impossible to explain. I believe in miracles but sometimes perhaps we need to look at things in a slightly different way. For Andrew, the miracle is perhaps not that he isn't with us today but that with such an aggressive disease he lived as long as he did. Andrew fought so hard and we prayed so hard. His insatiable will to live meant that he died in October rather than February, and that extra time has made all the difference.

We need to understand that healing comes through death, just as much as through a physical restoration of the body to full health. As my friend Janet said when she wrote to me not long after Andrew's death.....

"When the ways of God seem incomprehensible, I find it useful to look at healing from two perspectives. Sometimes the illness is taken away from the person, at others the person is taken away from the illness. In Andy's case I am sure it was the latter..."

This does not mean we shouldn't pray for people to get better. God wants us to pray for people to get well and if we are defeatist in the way we pray, we put God in a box, and question his ability to do the miraculous. However, if we understand that when we die we are freed from our pain and our suffering and are made whole by being united with Christ, it will help us to rejoice for those who have gone ahead of us.

I cannot begin to imagine what heaven is like. But for Andrew, heaven is the reward for his faith, courage and bravery. This is why my sorrow and sadness can be tempered with confidence and joy:

No eye has seen,
No ear has heard,
No mind has conceived,
What God has prepared for those who love him.

(1 Corinthians 2 v9)

MEDICAL GLOSSARY

ABLC (Amphotericin B Lipid Complex)
An antifungal drug, less toxic on the kidneys.

Adenoids
Two masses of tissue situated at the back of the nose. Part of the lymphatic system.

Amphotericin
Antifungal drug given in a bag to treat fungal infections. It is yellow.

Bone Marrow
Spongey tissue found in the bone from which the blood is produced.

Bone Marrow Aspirate
Tests to see if abnormal cells are present in the bone marrow.

Central Venous Catheter
Catheter inserted into a central vein e.g neck vein to enable a prolonged and reasonably easy access to the circulation.

Cerebro-Spinal Fluid
Fluid in the brain and spine

Cheyne Stoke Respiration
A sign of respiratory distress when the patients breathing is of a wax and wane pattern.

C.T. Scan (Computer Aided Tomography)
A special computerized serial x-ray study to allow more accurate and 2 dimensional definition of any abnormality.

Fluconazole
An antifungal drug

Fungal Septicaemia
A fungal infection in the blood

GCSF (Granulocyte Cell Stimulating Factor)
Hormone used to promote growth of white cells.

GMCSF (Granulocyte Macrophage Cell Stimulating Factor)
Variation on the above, but in addition also stimulates Macrophages.

Gentamicin
A broad spectrum antibiotic drug.

Hickman Catheter
Type of central line used to administer chemotherapy and antibiotics

High Grade, T-Cell Lymphoblastic Non-Hodgkins Lymphoma
A very aggressive type of Lymphoma. As a whole the complete remission rate after chemotherapy is approaching 50 - 60%. However, the long term survival rate is only around 30%. This is speaking in general terms because the response and the cure rate depends on the stage of the disease and associated prognostic factors.

Intrathecally
Injection into the base of the spine

Intravenous
Through the vein.

Lumbar Puncture
Test to see if abnormal cells are present in the Cerebro-Spinal Fluid.

MRI Scan (Magnetic Resonance Imaging)
A non-invasive technique to allow more accurate assessment of abnormality than a CT Scan.

Melaena
Bleeding through the bowels.

Neurotoxic
Damaging to the nerves.

Neutrophils
Particular white cells most significant in fighting infection.

Non-Hodgkins Lymphoma
A malignant disease of the Lymph Glands. This can be slow
growing (low grade) or fast growing (high grade).

Peripheral Neuropathy
Abnormal pathology affecting nerves from the spinal cord.

Piperacillin
A broad spectrum, Penicillin type antibiotic.

Platelets
Cells used to clot the blood.

Pleural Effusion
Fluid found on the walls of the lungs.

Sub-cutaneous
Under the skin.

Superior Vena Cava (SVC)
The major vein supplying venous blood into the right atrium

Total Parenteral Nutrition (TPN)
Large white bag of nutrients given intravenously to maintain
normal levels of nutrients if the patient is not eating.

APPENDIX

The information contained in these newsletters was correct as was known when they were produced in 1995.

In the light of information gathered after Andrew's death and while writing this book, there may be some inaccuracies contained within these newsletters.

As far as we are aware at the time of writing, the accurate account of Andrew's treatment is contained within the main body of the book

NEWSLETTERS

Andy Ridge   25-2-95

Andy started off the week not too bad, but still with fluid on his stomach. This has been drained and has not returned as bad. He got rather agitated and anxious Tuesday evening and Mike has stayed with him throughout the nights this week.

Andy is receiving treatment called 'G.C.S.F.' Put simply he is being given drugs to promote production of white blood cells to help his body fight the infection. Andy has also been suffering from vivid nightmares about dying, which I believe are not helped by a high temperature which at one time was around 40°C. Thankfully this is being brought under control now and he's sleeping much better from that point of view.

The main 'crisis' this week has been the appearance of a fungal infection which has set him back, but the doctors are in the process of treating that.

Speaking to Mike on Thursday (23rd) he said "Andy's amazing. he just 'won't lie down' He's determined to fight it" Andy has a big battle ahead of him, so if we can make it easier for him then so much the better.

The power of prayer has amazed all of us who have been praying for him in church this week. As we all feel so helpless in this situation we have seen the power of God working through our prayers with the reports from Mike of Andy's improvement that day.

Prayer points for the coming week.
The continuing G.C.S.F. treatment. The next 7 - 10 days are critical. If successful it will be a significant step forward. Talking to Mike on Saturday afternoon he tells me that the white blood cell count is up which is encouraging.
Prayer is also needed for this fungal infection. Let's pray that the drugs will work as quickly as possible.
Speaking to Mike on Friday night he said that the hospital have been in contact with the United States regarding some new drug which has had positive results over there, and as we were speaking they were being flown over here for Andy at a cost of

thousands of dollars, so they're pulling the stops out for him. Let's pray that these will go a long way to a cure.

General prayers for Andy in that he doesn't have any more setbacks, but if he does that they may not be too serious. The main things are:- Temperature, Nightmares and he seems to be his lowest in the mornings, and also prayer for the long nights. As we all know the nights are the worst.

Not forgetting Mike as well. Andy gets considerable Christian support from Mike as he feels more at ease with him. Mike spends the night with him, so prayer for refreshing sleep for him also.

If you know of anyone who would like to join us in the evenings, a reminder that we pray every weekday evening from 9pm -10pm in church. Please try to make it if you can, but be warned, it's cold, so wrap up well. If you can't come along your prayers at any time will be more than appreciated especially when we're praying at 9pm.

Andy Ridge   4-3-95

Trust in the Lord with all your heart. Proverbs 3:5

Every evening I contact Mike to get the latest news of Andy's condition and on Tuesday evening the above sentence was printed at the bottom of the piece of paper I was using. Who says God never speaks to us!

Thankfully this past week has been a lot more positive. Andy has a new consultant now, but his original consultant, Dr Chu, popped in to see him on Saturday morning and said that he looked a lot better and was pleased with his progress. They have had Andy up and about a little this week to help him get a bit of strength back into his legs and at one point they had him using a Zimmer frame. "Doesn't do much for your street cred" was one comment I heard! The swelling in his stomach and arms has gone down due to the fact that they're giving him Warfarin to thin his blood down. Also the fluid on his lungs has stayed static and the doctors don't seem too concerned about it although they are probably going to drain it sometime next week. His temperature is stable and he's eating better. He has also been moved out of a private room and is back in the main ward again now. So on the whole, a lot better picture this week.

Prayer points for the coming week

Andy is going to be on the anti-fungal drug for another week to clear up the infection, so prayer for its continued success.

Andy needs a lot of strength as he is hopefully going to start the next stage of his chemotherapy in 2 weeks. Please pray that it will be more successful.

Prayer would also be appreciated for his mobility and also that he can get a bit more food down him. He is eating but they would like him to eat a bit better than he has been doing to enable him to gain his strength to walk.

General prayers also for a continued upward and positive swing. Things are looking better, but there is still a long way to go.

Andy Ridge   11-3-95

Andy's condition improved this week. He's been enjoying food, rather than having to eat for eating sake and his temperature has been stabilised, a good sign as the doctors say that this is how they can tell the fungal infection is being killed off. He had the last of the anti-fungal antibiotic on Saturday.

There has been one setback this week. On Monday night Andy was passing blood. They gave him platelets and clotting agents and fortunately this had stopped by Wednesday.

They are now in a position to start treating the cancer again now. Phase 2 of the chemotherapy was started on Friday and that will last for 4 weeks subject to no more infections.

A few weeks ago the Pathfinders sent him a tape which he enjoyed immensely. I had one report that the nurses were putting in a drip for him to the Pathfinders singing "Who's the King of the Jungle?" It seems the tape has had all the medical staff laughing. He's also enjoyed a Jazz CD from his friends and colleagues from Durham.

Lynn and I visited Andy on Saturday afternoon to find him asleep as he'd had some sleeping tablets the night before, but he did awake eventually and we were pleasantly surprised at how well he looked compared to the last time I saw him 8 weeks ago.

Prayer points for the week ahead

The main point for prayer will be the success of the next phase of Andy's chemotherapy. Please pray that it will be a major step forward for him and that he has no more infections or setbacks.

Prayer is also needed that Andy will get a better appetite and mobility in the coming weeks.

There has been a lot to thank God for this week. Andy is still seriously ill and there's still a long way to go. but with God, all things are possible (Mark 10 v27)

Andy Ridge   26-3-95

I am pleased to report that there was better news this week. On Monday night Mike arrived at the prayer meeting to tell us that Andy had had a chest X-ray and the results showed that his lungs were free from fluid. As this is related to the disease, the doctors are encouraged by this response to the chemotherapy. He has also gone back to the main ward as from last Monday (20th).

Last Friday (24th) the prayer group thought it would be good to give thanks for some good news after the ups and downs of the past 3 months and we had an impromptu worship and prayer evening, thoroughly enjoyed by all who attended.

Prayer points for the week ahead

The main concern this week is Andy's loss of weight. The doctors have put him on a course of "T.P.N." (Intravenous Nutrition) to try to stabilise his weight. Please pray this will be successful.

He also has 2 more weeks of this phase of chemotherapy to go. Please pray that it'll go smoothly without any infections, and that he'll have a good response to the treatment.

Finally, Andy would appreciate your prayers to keep his spirits up.

Andy Ridge   1-4-95

This week the doctors have decided to give Andy a break from the chemotherapy. He's completed 75% of Phase 2 and they're quite pleased with his response. Hopefully in the 2- 3 week break this will enable him to get his strength back and to put on some weight. His temperature has still been fluctuating so he's still on antibiotics, although this is mainly as a precaution. Andy's chest X-ray last Sunday again showed the absence of fluid which is good news.

The nurses have provisionally talked about Andy coming home for a night or a day at the end of next week to give him a break as he's been in hospital for 2 months now and a break would do him the world of good.

Andy is on a moving bed which helps with his physiotherapy. He is strapped in and the bed can be lifted upright so he can get some weight on his feet. Professor Cawley came round to ask what he was doing. Andy replied "My Physio!" to which the Prof replied "In that case carry on!"

Prayer points for the week ahead

1. The main point for prayer this week is for the T.P.N., his eating and to stabilise his weight. Let's pray that this will be effective.

2. Andy has been free of infections this time. Prayer is needed that this will continue.

3. Prayer would be very much appreciated for Andy's day at home. Let's hope that if he is able to come home that he will have a good day and that he can appreciate it and also that we have some fine weather to cheer him up.

Andy Ridge   8-4-95

This week has been an up and down week for Andy. We had the good news early on that his weight had increased from 44.6Kg to 50.4Kg after nearly two weeks of T.P.N. Also Andy's chest X-ray on Wednesday shows a tiny bit of fluid on his left lung which is still pleasing. He is in the second week of his break from chemotherapy, but has been passing diahorrea and blood and still has a fluctuating temperature. Professor Cawley feels he has picked up a common infection and he is being treated with several antibiotics including Amphotericin. Remarkably Andy has been bright and in good spirits for most of the week. Let's pray that he continues to have such a positive attitude.

Prayer points for the week ahead

1. That Andy's temperature will begin to stabilise as his antibiotics start to take effect.

2. That Andy's passing of blood (side effect of chemo) may stop as a result of platelets, transfusions and clotting factors.

3. That Andy will continue to be in good spirits and that he will be able to start back on his chemotherapy on 17th April.

4. That Andy's T.P.N. will continue to help him put on weight and his mobility will continue to improve with regular physio.

I'd like to thank everyone who has been praying or have taken these newsletters about Andy as I know he very much appreciates it. Andy would like to thank everyone who has written, and I know he still appreciates mail.

Andy Ridge   15-4-95

This week has proved difficult for Andy. Unfortunately he has picked up another fungal infection and is being treated with ABLC (Amphotericin) the anti-fungal antibiotic and several other antibiotics. His temperature continues to fluctuate, and because his blood counts are very low the consultant, Professor Cawley, has started Andrew on GCSF hormone treatment to boost the amount of white blood cells which help fight infection.

On the positive side his platelets (which help the blood clot) are OK and the incidence of passing blood has seemed to have subsided for the moment. Andy has been bright and in good spirits for most of the week, although he had some pain in his stomach Friday afternoon.

On Saturday afternoon Andy was able to be taken out for a few hours. I hear that he was taken over to the Wirral and enjoyed it immensely although he was rather tired when he got back and was asleep when I phoned.

Prayer points for the week ahead

1. That Andrew's fungal infection will be effectively dealt with by the Amphotericin and his temperature will subside.

2. The GCSF treatment will produce good results as it did previously, and increase Andrew's white cells to help fight his infection.

3. That Andrew's T.P.N. will continue to strengthen him and provide adequate nutrition.

4. That Andrew's platelets and blood pressure will remain satisfactory so that he has no further incidents of passing blood.

Andy Ridge   22-4-95

Over the past few weeks I have had help with the newsletters from Mike, but this week it falls to me alone to write the report. Mike has taken a well earned holiday in Cyprus for a week as he needed to get away. I hope he's having better weather than we are at the moment.

As for Andy, I have unfortunately been out of touch with things this week as I have had to hand over the organisation of the prayers this week to Martin Haddock. I think Andy's had a fairly good week, and he's not started his chemotherapy again yet. As it's been holiday time I believe he's had lots of visitors which has cheered him up, and although he's still got the infection he's been quite bright and upbeat.

Prayer points for the coming week

As I've been away from everything this week I think the best prayers we can ask for are for Andy's continued progress back to full health and a lasting cure. Although his condition has stabilised from the problems he has been having he still needs our prayers to get him through the illness. Let's pray that Andy will have a swift and permanent cure.

Andy Ridge   30-4-95

Andy continues to have a fluctuating temperature and so he continues to receive the anti-fungal ABLC (Amphotericin). Fortunately his blood counts have all come up so he is able to fight his infection with natural means as well as antibiotics.
Professor Cawley came round last Thursday and reported a slight improvement of his chest infection on the latest X-ray. Andrew's legs continue to ache periodically so he is to have a special nuclear scan on Monday to assess if there has been any damage to his nerves. He continues to receive intravenous nutrition and his appetite is slowly getting better.

Prayer points for the week ahead

1. That the antibiotics and infection fighting cells (neutrophils) will continue to fight Andrew's fungal infection and that it will be clear as soon as possible.

2. That Andrew's temperature will become stabilised and he will be able to go back on chemotherapy as soon as possible.

3. That there will be a positive outcome from Andy's NMR scan on Monday. Also that his legs will get stronger like his arms have done.

4. Andy continues to be positive and chatty - pray that his attitude, which is important, continues to be the same.

Andy Ridge   7-5-95

This week has been a crucial week for Andrew as his new consultant, Dr Clark and the team, reassess his disease and his response to the treatment so far. Concern about Andrew's aching legs prompted the doctor's to send him for an MR Scan on his lumbar spine on Tuesday - the results are positive, there is nothing untoward and Andrew continues to go down to the gym for regular physio. He has put on weight (46.8 - 49Kg) and the latest chest X-ray reveals that his chest infection is slowly clearing up. Although his white cell count is high, on close inspection the doctors report that there are lots of normal cells and not just abnormal (or cancer cells) as was feared. As this newsletter goes to press we crucially await the results of Andrew's CT scan and bone marrow sample - this will give us a more accurate picture of his response to chemotherapy so far.

Andy has been out to experience the joys of Liverpool in 23º sunshine this week - he is able, once assisted into his wheelchair, to wheel himself around. He had an unassisted wash and shave and continues to be positive, confident and in good spirits.

Although his temperature continues to fluctuate this appears to be related more to his disease than his infection and it is not making him feel unwell.

Prayer points for the week ahead

1. A positive response, which is critical, to the bone marrow sample and CT scan.

2. A continued strengthening of Andy's body as his T.P.N. (nutrition) and physiotherapy continues.

3. That when strong enough Andrew's chemotherapy will be successful in killing malignant cells.

4. That Andrew continues to be buoyant and encouraged by the nurses and prayers of support from all around.

Andy Ridge   14-5-95

Apart from one day when Andrew was feeling a bit down it has been another encouraging week for him. He still has a fungal infection on his chest which takes a notoriously long time to get rid of, but this is slowly clearing up, and the doctors have put his antibiotics onto alternate days as a response to this slow improvement. He has slightly increased his weight and the CT scan and bone marrow sample have had positive results in that the Haematologists are satisfied with his response to the chemotherapy so far.

Andrew has been referred to a Youth Rehabilitation Centre in either Broadgreen or Fazakerley Hospitals by his consultant Dr Clark. If he is accepted he will go there for a period of intensive physiotherapy and building up his general condition which is still very weak before he goes back to Liverpool for further treatment.

Prayer points for the week ahead

1. The T.P.N. (nutrition) will continue to have good effect, and with an increasing appetite Andrew may continue to put on weight.

2. That the process of referral and being able to leave the Royal to go for physiotherapy and rehabilitation will be a quick one and that once there Andy may be able to adjust and start to make real progress with his legs.

3. An end to his fungal infection, which has dragged on for about a month. Pray that the antibiotics will help to finish it off.

Andy Ridge   20-5-95

Andy has had a good week and is continuing to make steady progress. He went out to the Wirral on Friday, and at the time of writing is planning on coming home to watch the Cup Final. His calcium levels were too high at the beginning of the week which was making him feel sick but these have been brought back to normal.

He continues, thankfully, to put on weight (49.3 to 51.8Kg) and is still receiving anti-fungal antibiotics on alternate days. Concern over Andrew's weakness in his legs has prompted the consultant neurologist to be called in to do some tests and investigations before Andrew goes to the Youth Rehabilitation Centre at Fazakerley or Broadgreen.

Prayer points for the week ahead

1. Andrew is due a chest X-ray on Monday. Let's pray that it reveals his chest infection is virtually cleared.

2. That the investigations by the neurologist will not reveal anything untoward with Andrew's nervous system in his legs.

3. That continued T.P.N. (nutrition) and an increasing appetite will help Andy to put on more weight.

4. He may remain positive and in good spirits.

Andy Ridge   28-5-95

Andy continues to remain in the Royal and is awaiting assessment by Fazakerley before he is moved to the Youth Rehabilitation Centre. The chest X-ray on Monday showed an improvement and Andrew has started a course of tablets which will be used to replace the ABLC (Anti-Fungal antibiotics) which has helped to clear his chest infection. The studies by the neurologist revealed severe damage to Andrew's nerve ends in his arms and legs. They are, however, hopeful that he will get his mobility back after a long period of time. His temperature is starting to get back into the normal range after about six weeks of mountain peaks. His weight is now 50.5Kg (Thursday)

Prayer points for the week ahead

1. A bed will be found and Andrew will be able to move to the Youth Rehabilitation Centre at Fazakerley as soon as possible.

2. Thank God for Andrew's slowly improving condition and that his infection has been beaten.

3. Pray for more mobility and strength in his legs as Andy's nerve ends take a long time to grow back.

4. T.P.N. (intravenous food) will continue to have a good effect on Andrew's general weight and condition.

Andy Ridge   4-6-95

This week has been a very encouraging week for Andy. After a 9 week break he has started back on a 'mild' course of chemotherapy. His chest X-ray continues to show an improving picture and he is due to come off ABLC (anti-fungal antibiotics) on Wednesday next week. His weight has increased from 50.5 to 53.2 kg and after 10 weeks of TPN he has been taken off intravenous food to encourage him to start eating again.
He has been home last Sunday and on Friday to enjoy home cooking and he has made progress with physiotherapy, making his first steps with support and a Zimmer frame on Thursday. Finally he received a visit yesterday morning from Dr Williams at Fazakerley who says he is an ideal candidate for the YDU and is therefore likely to move at the end of next week.

Prayer points for the week ahead

1. Thank God for the progress Andy has made and pray that he will settle into the new atmosphere of Fazakerley and continue to make progress.

2. That Andrew's chemotherapy will help to keep on top of his disease and kill off malignant cells.

3. He will be able to eat well to put on weight and that his appetite will slowly come back.

4. He will continue to make progress with physiotherapy to increase his leg muscles and general mobility.

Andy Ridge   13-6-95

This week has been an encouraging week for Andrew. On Tuesday he had an emotional farewell with the staff of 7Y after being on the ward for nearly 22 weeks. The nurses all queued up to give him a farewell kiss and there was a lovely goodbye card presented to him. Dr Chu also came in to say goodbye although Andrew will have to attend Clinic on the 23rd June with Dr Clark to see how his treatment is going. He arrived at the Younger Disabled Unit on Tuesday afternoon and has started to settle down to the new environment. He will receive a personal course of physiotherapy and occupational therapy in order to get him built up and to remove the contractures in his legs.

He gets dressed and goes in his wheelchair for meals and fortunately the food has got the thumbs up so far! He is still on anti-fungal tablets and chemotherapy tablets but his line has been removed and he is free to go wherever he wants once in his wheelchair.

Prayer points for the week ahead

1. Chemotherapy will continue to have a good effect in killing malignant cells and keeping on top of the disease.

2. Andrew will soon be fully settled down to the new environment at Fazakerley and will make progress with his course of physiotherapy.

3. He will continue to regain his appetite and maintain a reasonable weight.

Andy Ridge   18-6-95

This week has been another positive week for Andy. He has settled down well in the new environment at Fazakerley and is making steady progress with his programme of Physio and occupational therapy. His weight remains fairly stable at 52.2kg and he is continuing to eat well and maintain his nutritional status. The doctor came to see him on Tuesday to inform him that his blood count results were good. He was home during the day last weekend and on Wednesday afternoon took part in a trip to Preston YDU for a Quiz afternoon and buffet. Lets pray that Andy continues to move in the right direction.

Prayer points for the week ahead.
1. Chemotherapy will continue to have a good effect in killing malignant cells and keeping on top of the disease.

2. Andrew will continue to make sound progress with his Physiotherapy and Exercises

3. He will continue to eat well and maintain a reasonable body weight.

Andy Ridge   25-6-95

Andy has had a good week as far as his physiotherapy and general care is concerned but his full blood count results on the Tuesday showed that his counts were quite low particularly his platelets. Dr Wright the Haematologist at Fazakerley has stopped his Chemotherapy on Wednesday morning and he was transferred to ward 20 for a blood transfusion on Wednesday night. He was due back in the unit on Thursday morning and is going to see Dr Chu on Friday morning at clinic. His temperature on Wednesday evening was normal at 36.9°c and Andy is continuing to eat well and planning to come home for the weekend.

Prayer points for the week ahead
1. Andy's blood counts would recover as a result of his blood transfusion. His blood would continue to respond to Chemotherapy.

2.His programme of Physiotherapy will continue to be successful in reducing the contractures in Andrew's legs.

3. He would continue to eat well to help maintain a stable body weight.

Andy Ridge   1-7-95

Andy has had a reasonable week, but as usual when he has made progress, there is usually some new setback that comes along. He has put on more weight (now 55kg) but he has picked up an outbreak of shingles on his back and has started a course of Acyclovir three times a day by infusion (anti-viral drug). He has also been put on an antibiotic because his white blood cell count is very low and he is therefore prone to infection. He continues to be in good spirits however and is still doing his programme of Physiotherapy and occupational therapy.

Prayer points for week ahead.

1. The Shingles will remain localised and may be effectively dealt with by Andy's course of Acyclovir.

2. He would be protected from infection by antibiotics until his white cells recover.

3. He would continue to eat well, maintain a normal temperature and make progress with his physiotherapy.

Andy Ridge   9-7-95

Andrew has had a reasonable week. His shingles are not as painful as they were at the weekend and they appear to be healing up fairly well. Dr Wright came to see him on Wednesday to tell him that his blood counts were slowly beginning to recover and the films of his blood were very good. He has recommended that Andrew's course of Acylovir be extended until Monday to make it a 10 day course. Andrew had a slight temperature on Wednesday night (37.6c) which is being monitored and blood cultures were taken to check for infection. He continues to eat well but has been in bed more this last week because he has a line in for intravenous treatment. His friends from Durham visited on Tuesday and he is planning on starting to write some letters to all those who have written to him.

Prayer points for the week ahead

1. Andrew's counts would continue to recover especially his white blood count which is crucial for fighting infection.

2. He would be protected from infection and his temperature would return to the normal range.

3. His shingles would continue to heal as infusions of Zovirax continue to have a good effect.

4. Despite having a line in his arm he will be able to move around and continue with some of his physiotherapy.

Andy Ridge   16-7-95

Andrew has had an encouraging week. He is currently enjoying his first weekend at home without having to go back to hospital, since February. His shingles are healing well and he continues on a course of Zovirax tablets till early next week. He has gained some more weight (56.5 Kg) and has made some good progress with his physiotherapy, moving up and down the corridors with a Zimmer frame and some support.

Prayer points for the week ahead

1. Andrew will continue to make good progress with his physiotherapy.

2. Andrew is likely to restart 'maintenance chemotherapy' this week. Pray that this will be successful in controlling his disease.

3. That Andrew will continue to eat well and be free from infections.

Andy Ridge   23-7-95

Andy has had a good week. He has worked hard with his physiotherapy and has been doing a lot of walking with the support of his Gutter frame. His blood count results were good and he was recommended his maintenance chemotherapy. He is due to see Dr Chu at clinic next Friday. His shingles have cleared up well and he has switched to maintenance Acyclovir tablets.

Prayer points for the week ahead

1. Andrew will continue to eat well to maintain his nutritional status.

2. He will continue to make excellent progress with his walking and will be able to use the Gutter frame as much as possible.

3. His maintenance chemotherapy would continue to keep on top of his disease.

Andy Ridge   30-7-95

It has been an excellent week of progress for Andrew. He celebrated his 25th birthday on Thursday with his family and walked into the house with his Zimmer frame on Friday evening to spend the weekend at home. The doctor reported at clinic that he is "most definitely" in remission which is wonderful news. He has been stopped antibiotics for the infection he had weeks ago. He continues on maintenance chemotherapy and his liver function is slowly returning to normal. He is making pleasing progress with his physiotherapy walking with a Zimmer frame and sometimes crutches and hoping to move onto walking sticks in the near future. His weight remains stable at 55.5 Kg.

Prayer points for the week ahead

1. Thank God for Andrew's first remission. Pray that this healthy state may continue in order to give Andrew time to regain his strength and be able to walk freely.

2. The effective use of Andrew's maintenance chemotherapy. Pray that it will continue to keep on top of Andrew's disease.

3. That Andrew may continue to make progress with his walking and his nutrition.

Andy Ridge   3-8-95

Andy continues to make progress with his walking, using only 2 sticks and using the exercise bike to strengthen his legs. His blood counts have been low and it appears that Andrew has a throat infection, with inflamed tonsils and swollen glands. He has been put on penicillin and some other antibiotic by Dr Wright and this will be reviewed on Monday. He continues on Mercaptopurine for maintenance chemotherapy. He enjoyed a trip out on the River Mersey on Thursday afternoon.

Prayer points for the week ahead

1. That Andrew's throat infection would clear up quickly in response to his antibiotics

2. Andrew is obviously concerned about his swollen glands in his neck. Prayer is needed that he would be reassured and that the swelling will subside in due course.

3. That Andrew's chemotherapy would continue to keep on top of his disease.

4. He would, despite the hot weather, continue to eat well to maintain a stable body weight.

Andy Ridge   10-8-95

Urgent Newsletter

This has been a very difficult and disappointing week for Andrew. It is a credit to him how well he has managed to cope with all the news. On Monday, Dr Wright the haematologist at Fazakerley decided to send Andrew back to the Royal for further investigations. These investigations have shown that Andrew has had a relapse and his disease has reappeared in his lymph glands around his neck and in his bone marrow. His chest X-ray revealed that his chest is clear at the moment. Dr Chu is obviously very disappointed with this news and has decided to put Andrew on a program of chemotherapy similar to the one he was on in January, before checking the bone marrow in four weeks time to see if there is any response. Of course some of the drugs Andrew had in January cannot be used again because of the damage they caused. The next 4 weeks are going to be very critical as far as the future is concerned. We would ask for a special effort on Andrew's behalf by all those who have prayed for him in the past.

Prayer points for the week ahead

1. That Andrew's chemotherapy drugs, prednisolone and daunorubicin will be effective in killing off malignant cells and getting back on top of Andrew's disease.

2. That he would remain free from infection. He is to have a course of low dose anti-fungal antibiotics to accompany his chemotherapy.

3. That he would continue to eat well, make progress with his walking and have a positive attitude to his treatment as well as trusting in God.

Andy Ridge   20-8-95

This weeks newsletter is rather short on details as Mike has been taking a well earned holiday in Rhodes, so it has fallen to me to tell you of Andy's condition.
I can only report that Andy is O.K. Before our prayer meetings at St John's I phone the hospital to find out Andy's condition that day to see if there are any pressing points for prayer. On Monday & Tuesday I spoke to Andy personally and he sounded well. He said that he'd had the results of a lumbar puncture and that they were OK. He asked if we could pray that he would be free from any infection during this course of treatment. When I'd phoned on Thursday I was told by the nurse that he was out and about walking round the hospital with his relatives.
As far as I am aware, Andy's appetite is good, so much so that on at least one occasion this week he has had fish and chips for his meal.
Unfortunately as I write this on Saturday night I have no new information, but normal service should be resumed for next week's newsletter.

Prayer points for the week ahead

I have no new points for prayer this week, except for Andy's request that he may be kept free from any infections that are about at the moment. Apart from this all we can do is pray that Andy's overall condition will improve and that he can make a full recovery.

Andy Ridge   27-8-95

A week of ups and downs for Andrew. He has increased his weight to about 58Kg and continues to be mobile walking with only one stick and going down for physiotherapy each day. Unfortunately there has been no clinical improvement in his swelling and Dr Chu is again disappointed as we are 2½ weeks into Phase I of the chemotherapy. It looks likely that Andrew will, barring infection, move onto Phase II of his chemotherapy although he will need to have an operation to put in a Hickman Catheter.

Prayer points for the week ahead

1. If there is no response to Phase I of chemotherapy let us pray, that as last time round, Phase II will be more successful.

2. That Andrew will continue to eat well, remain mobile and keep free from serious infection.

3. That Andrew's operation to put in a Hickman Catheter will go smoothly on Wednesday.

Andy Ridge   3-9-95

Andy has had a difficult week. His neck, tonsils and adenoids remain enlarged and have proved resistant to Phase I chemotherapy. A Central Venous Catheter has eventually been inserted after great difficulty and much answer to prayer. He is to attend a 2 week course of Radiotherapy at Clatterbridge, following a meeting with the consultant radiologist on Friday morning. Whatever happens the way ahead is looking difficult with no guarantees and no simple solutions. Andrew continues to eat and maintain a stable temperature. We went down to chapel on Thursday night after talking to Dr Chu and gave the situation to God.

Prayer points for the week ahead

1. That the emergency radiotherapy will be effective in destroying malignant lymphoma cells in Andrew's neck and tonsils.

2. Phase 2 chemotherapy will be able to go ahead in 2 weeks time.

3. That Andrew would remain free from serious infection and especially that the line would remain infection free.

4. He would be aware of God's love and presence during these critical 2 weeks.

Andy Ridge   10-9-95

Andrew has had an encouraging week and is feeling better. He attended Clatterbridge Centre for Oncology on Monday, but as his blood counts are low the consultant radiologist decided against a progressive course of treatment at this stage. He did however have a high dose of Cobalt 60 Radiation and is due to see the Radiologist at clinic on Friday morning. His swallowing is easier and his swollen neck is coming down so hopefully these are encouraging signs. Andrew had a temperature on Wednesday and the blood cultures which were taken have grown a bacterial infection which is not serious and is being treated with several antibiotics. Professor Cawley came round on Thursday and said that once Andrew's tonsils have shrunk further Chemotherapy is needed and they are thinking of giving Andrew a new course of treatment but this will have to be discussed at length with Dr Chu.

Prayer points for the week ahead

1. Andrew will respond well to his Radiotherapy and further courses will be possible as his blood counts recover.

2. He will remain free from the serious fungal infections of the past.

3. He will continue to eat well in order to maintain his nutritional status and will continue to remain mobile.

4. He would continue to trust God for the future and his faith will remain strong.

Andy Ridge   17-9-95

I am pleased to report that Andrew has responded very well to his initial dose of Radiotherapy. He attended Clatterbridge on Monday afternoon. His blood counts are starting to recover but as happened last week, he had a temperature and the blood cultures have grown a bacterial infection which is being treated with several antibiotics. Professor Cawley feels that now Andrew's tonsils are shrinking a Hickman Catheter should be put in next week and then Andrew will be able to start a new course of chemotherapy called "Mini BEAM" which is used in the treatment of high grade lymphomas.
Andrew has been in good spirits all week and continues to eat well and exercise his legs.

Prayer points for the week ahead

1. Andrew will continue to respond to his radiotherapy.

2. He will remain free from the serious fungal infections of the past.

3. Andrew's new course of chemotherapy. Pray that this new assortment of drugs would be successful in killing Lymphoblasts and putting Andrew in remission.

4. His operation to put in an abdominal Hickman line would go smoothly next week.

Andy Ridge   24-9-95

Andrew went down to theatre on Monday morning and has had a smooth operation to insert an abdominal Hickman line. Apart from being a bit sore on Monday night, there have been no problems with the new line and it has been used for platelet support and antibiotics. On Thursday Andrew commenced a six day course of chemotherapy which is very aggressive. We are hoping and praying for a good response to these new drugs and a smoother ride than the stormy course of treatment Andrew had at the beginning of the year. Andrew is receiving antibiotics and his weight remains stable at 56Kg. His steroids are being reduced slowly in order to prevent serious infection. Andrew remains as positive and determined as usual. We committed the new treatment and the future to God at chapel on Wednesday evening.

Prayer points for the week ahead

1. That Andrew's new course of treatment will kill off malignant lymphoblasts and get back on top of the disease.

2. He will remain free from the serious infections of the past.

3. Andrew will adjust to the new position of his Hickman line and it will remain free from infection.

4. He will continue to trust God for the future and his faith will remain strong.

Andy Ridge   1-10-95

Andrew has had a week of ups and downs but fortunately was ending the week feeling better. His course of chemotherapy ended on Tuesday and it will now take about 3-4 weeks for his blood counts to recover. He has had a persistent fever and was feeling very poorly on Wednesday. Although at the moment the doctors are not certain about the source of infection, Andrew has been put on a daily course of stronger Amphotericin and his temperature was starting to plateau on Thursday. The chest X-rays taken on Monday and Wednesday have both been clear and Professor Cawley feels that although the likely cause of the temperature is an infection, he is on a strong regime of antibiotics which should cover all angles. Andrew continues to be mobile and his eating is satisfactory. He is likely to remain in hospital because he has no white cells and is having regular transfusions of blood and platelets.

Prayer points for the week ahead

1. That Andrew's active anticancer drugs will kill off malignant Lymphoblasts and get back on top of the disease.

2. His strong regime of antibiotics will help fight infection and stabilise his temperature

3. Andrew's Hickman line will remain infection free.

Andy Ridge   8-10-95

Andy has had a reasonable week. Although his temperature is at a lower level than the week before, it is still above normal and it appears that the source of this is a chest infection. He is on strong regime antibiotics including a daily dose of Amphotericin (anti-fungal). This antibiotic is toxic and causes a loss of potassium so Andrew is also having bags of potassium in order to keep this potassium at a reasonable level. The chest X-ray taken on Friday showed no deterioration which is encouraging. Andy has also been suffering from heartburn and acid in his stomach which is making him feel unwell and unable to eat a great quantity. At the moment his weigh remains stable at 58kg. Andrew's blood counts remain very low so we are unable to assess his response to chemotherapy at the moment. He managed to get home on Thursday evening for a break from the ward.

Prayer points for the week ahead

1. That Andrew's active anti-cancer drugs will continue to kill malignant cells and help the doctors to get back on top of his disease.

2. His strong regime of antibiotics will successfully help fight off this infection and reduce Andy's temperature.

3. His upset stomach will respond to medication and ease in the coming week.

4. He will continue to be in positive mood, and his faith in God will remain strong.

Andy Ridge   15-10-95

Andy has had a satisfactory week. He got home on Wednesday afternoon but was very tired and has been sleeping a lot this week. He has a very sore throat which is being treated with a powerful pain killer which causes drowsiness as a side effect. Andrew's chest X-ray on Thursday has shown no change. His antibiotic has been changed to a 300 mg dose of ABLC (a lipid complex of Amphotericin) in order to combat his chest infection. Andrew has also commenced GCSF hormone treatment in order to boost his neutrophils which are essential to fight infection. Andrew will have to wait for 1 - 2 weeks for his counts to return before a CT scan and Bone Marrow are taken to assess his response to the chemotherapy.

Prayer points for the week ahead

1. Andrew's chemotherapy will have been successful in killing off many malignant cells.

2. Andrew's sore throat will ease in response to pain killers and improving blood counts.

3. His new regime of antibiotics (ABLC) will have an effect on reducing Andy's temperature to within the therapeutic range.

4. He will continue to fight his disease and his faith in God will remain strong.